Me Mam's Not In

Edwin S Towe

First published 2001 by Acorn Publications, Newark

ISBN: 1 903263 34 4

Introduction

The writer was born in 1924. The only son of a Yorkshire (Man of the soil) On demobilisation after the Great War, he had moved down to the coal fields of East Midshire to get work and a better wage. No one had realised the Miners strike in 1924 or the General strike lasting a year in 1926 was due.

My earliest recollection was of painful ears. I learned many years later parents were in the habit of pushing me through metal railings at the end of our miniature garden into the recreation ground. (The Rec.) I must have grown fast that day, on the way back I got my head stuck. By all accounts they were weeks digging rust shale and flaked paint out of my ears.

Just why they had christened me Ronald Albert Francis Chapman I never did find out. Children were never allowed to ask questions.

All through school, the R.A.F. initials amused everyone, soon my nick name was Raff among the boys, Ron by the girls, and either 'ee' or 'im by Dad.

On leaving school at fourteen years of age, I was fortunate enough to gain employment with a large Garage in the local town. My title was 'Apprentice Motor Mechanic'. In no time at all I befriended the senior to me Eric Towser. My first REAL learning period I now realise.

Work started for me a few months before the outbreak of WW2 (IN SHORTS). Before the week was out I had been bought a pair of second hand trousers, as the pores in my legs were full of spots of dirty oil etc.

Mum almost burst into tears when she realised that her 'little lad had grown up'.

Long heavy hours at work, plus joining the Air Training Corps as soon as it was formed. To say the least, every day was very full. Many work days were twelve hour shifts, plus a cycle ride of five miles each way, all for SIX SHILLINGS!! a week. Nights not spent at work were used for A.T.C. parades. Sundays, a morning swim, afternoons keeping (or getting) fit. Saturday nights dancing, after parades chasing the girls. The word boredom did not exist.

Thanks

Sincere thanks for the help I had from Anne, and Jean.

Last but by no means least, my wife. She has put up with my despair, tantrums, temper, without a moan. On so many occasions she has stopped me wanging the word processor through the kitchen window in desperation.

The word processor and the window are still intact.

ME MAM'S NOT IN
(Almost an auto biography)

Chapter 1
In At The Deep End

She must have been in her late twenties, not fat, but firm
and interestingly rounded. Her full breast at each breath
was doing its best to pop the fourth button of her size too
small blouse. The third button should have been fastened,
the fourth was well and truly, under pressure. All the
button holes were well worn. At each intake of breath,
the fourth button promised to release. I could not take
my eyes off it, and I had an uncomfortable feeling that
she knew it...

I had been released from the Royal Air Force just
over a year ago now. No intentions whatever of
returning to the garage where I had been apprenticed as a
motor mechanic. The very thoughts of all that filth, dirty
oil, kow towing to every Tom Dick and Harry that had
somehow or other got themselves a car. Once car owners,
some seemed to think of themselves as superior beings.
They spoke to and treated everyone in the trade as though
they were dirt beneath their feet. Mind you, that was how
the owners and garage management had treated us. The
actual owner, a small fat grey man with a grey moustache
hardly ever spoke to the 'slaves' as we called ourselves.
He would invariably speak to the manager who in turn
spoke to the foreman to pass on instructions. He was a
chain smoker, a Player's cigarette always in the centre of

his mouth, somehow, he managed to speak through it. His moustache was stained ginger in the centre. An uncouth, even if wealthy man. It was all "yes sir, no sir, three bags full sir" Is there any wonder most of us had not wished to return to that life?

No doubt, war is terrible, but in the experience of the lucky ones, who returned home alive, and with all their limbs intact. It was the chance to get away from the almost Dickension life all had experienced previously. During my own service life, I had savoured thoughts of becoming a salesman. My own idea of a salesman, was of one who drove a modern company car, wore a good suit, and cruised around the countryside with a car full of samples.

Within hours of arriving home from India I had spotted an advert in the local rag, an application letter was soon on its way. Not even demobbed yet, but I was expecting a call to attend Wharton for demobilisation within days, and the need to earn money was paramount.

The telegram arrived instructing me to attend R.A.F Wharton on the following Monday, I was back home complete with demob suit, papers, and thirty three pounds seventeen shillings and twopence clutched in my little hot hand by Tuesday tea time. Wednesday morning a letter arrived instructing me to attend the job interview at nine a.m. Thursday. It was all almost as hectic as service life.

Imagine my surprise, when after being accepted for the post, I was told to meet the Supervisor, with my push bike, at the Coffee Pot Cafe in the centre of a small town called Smeeton. Further surprise, when I was told the start time would be three thirty p.m. the following Friday!

Naturally. I   arrived at the cafe   early. (R.A.F. training?) It was a long worrying wait. In fact it was three cigarettes, two buns and three cups of tea long. Was I at the right place? What would he look like? How would we know each other? I was sweating with worry. Then he arrived, no doubts at all, a well set up man, over six feet tall, dark brown wavy hair, a good sports coat, well cut wool gabardine trousers, highly polished brogue shoes. A very good looking man. He came straight towards me. How did he know I was the person he wanted? He walked forward with his hand outstretched, a firm hand grip. He muttered as he glanced at his watch. "How's that for time keeping then? Have you been waiting long?"

I glanced at my own timepiece, spot on three thirty. "Guess I was early to play safe." I muttered, wondering just how early, and how safe, I had been.

He instructed, "Call me John," before ordering two teas and motioning that we should go to the rear of the cafe away from the local yokels.

"Have you any ideas about this work?" He questioned. I had to shake my head.

"Motor mechanic before I joined up, then a Wireless Mechanic in the R.A.F. till last week," I admitted.

John sipped at his tea, then putting the cup down, he pointed out. "It's simple really, you sell the public anything you can, then collect their money weekly, on the basis of a shilling per week, for each pound they owe."

"Anything?" I queried, really puzzled.

John laughed. "Almost, we don't sell cars or aeroplanes, but we do sell all clothing and household goods." With a quirky grin, he went on. "That's the easy part, the more difficult situation is to keep the good payers in debt, and get your money from the bad payers." I must have been struggling, looking blank, or thick, Super smiled.

"Drink up, we will get started. I think it will be easier for you to do it than for me to try to explain at this stage."

We cycled along the Main Street, me following behind, very deep in thought. A most interesting street, all very small shops. packed close together, every one looked to 'specialise' in some trade or other. I did not see a single Company or Ltd., sign painted above the small windows. It was all 'Tyler' the Plumber. 'Grice' Electrical goods. 'Gregson' camera specialist. 'Hazlewood' gents' hairdresser, Clarke's furnishers etc. My thoughts were interrupted as John called over his shoulder.

"Keep in your mind where we go, you will be on your own the week after next."

Right at the first island, left at the second, then almost immediately right up a slight hill. I just had time to note it was called Barsic Lane, before I almost ran into him as he dismounted.

"We start here," he announced.

For some peculiar reason I had a little trouble getting the bike to stand at the kerb edge. By the time I had done so, John had rapped hard on a door, opened it, and walked in. He called out "Solomons," in a loud voice whilst letting me in. Through another door at the end of a short passage, and into a kitchen, a hot kitchen. A huge fire was roaring up the chimney of a typical kitchen stove. All gleaming black lead and burnished steel. A bare wood scrubbed table in the centre of the room, two equally bare and scrubbed kitchen chairs, one each side of the table. A large, hard looking man was in the one with its back to us. He swivelled in his chair, a mug of hot tea in one hand, a half smoked Woodbine in the other.

"Yerv'e just missed 'er, she's gone to 'er Muther's. Yer'll 'ave ter call on yer road back."

"Could you not pay us to save a back call?" From a hopeful John..

"Not on yer bloody life, be t' last I seed on it if I did."

John led the way out. "My own fault for drinking tea in the cafe," he chuntered.

We both remounted our bikes and rode off again, me still in the rear, keeping a discreet silence and distance. Within a few yards John dismounted again. I was more on the ball this time, in fact was at the door as quick as he. Again the sharp rap on the door, followed by his strident call.

"Solomons."

"It's on the draining board," called out a strong female voice.

"Can I come in and introduce your new traveller?" John called out in return.

"Another bogger, what the bloody hell do you do with them?" came through an inner door before she burst through it. A really big lady, at least six feet tall, shoulders like a barn door, and bare arms like hams. She placed her hands on her hips and looked at me as though she might consider making an offer for me.

"Now that's a lot better, I did not like, or trust, that last shifty looking bugger you sent. Will you stick it lad?" She questioned.

"I-I think so," I almost stammered the reply.

"You'll have to toughen up son, or these bitches round here will have your guts for garters before you know it." She grinned at John, then looking back at me, queried, "Both ex R.A.F.?" We almost nodded in unison, puzzled.

"Thought so, you're both pretty like my baby brother, he did not come back from his thirteenth op. She blinked rapidly. "Navigator on Lancs," she explained with some difficulty. "In fact he was almost as blonde as you. Without that quiff in your hair, you would almost be his double."

I muttered a sort of "sorry to hear it," John admitted that he too was a Lanc. Navvy. but with only six ops. under his belt, almost apologising for the fact. I was now looking at John with new respect, when I realised she was expecting me to speak.

"Er, sorry, I was not good enough for aircrew, the eyes let me down and they made me into a wireless mechanic instead."

"No matter, you're both still alive." Fully recovered by now, she handed John her pass book and a ten shilling note whilst saying, "You're well over a stone overweight, too many aircrew breakfasts? It's no good being good looking, with green eyes and dark wavy hair if you're fat." John blushed and grinned as he returned her book.

What an introduction to the real world. A village school, with strict teachers, a strict Dad. Followed by the harsh mechanics training, almost five years in the forces all discipline of the highest order, all the squalor of India, now the seamy side of home. Almost every possible trade, Miners, knitters, seamers. All local trades, stockings, underwear, jumpers, with all the attendant ancillaries trades to keep them going. Precision engineers, electricians, plumbers, painters etc. A true hotch potch of the British working life.

Drunks, gamblers, liars, wife beaters on the one hand, yet others, so honest, so hard working. Talk about from the sublime to the ridiculous. By the end of the week I was beginning to enjoy this new challenge.

Next week, I was in charge of the money, with John looking on. Feeling very full of my own importance, the following Friday night, I knocked, and we both walked into a crowded kitchen. Dad, and four big teen age lads sat round the tin bath in the front of the fire, each with a sheet of the evening paper. Mam was just pouring more hot water from the fireside boiler into the bath, in which sat a very well blessed teenage daughter. The young lady sponged herself without concern, oblivious to all. We took their money and beat a hurried blushing exit.

Chapter 2
I Think They Call It Finding Your Feet

One of the first hard lessons was learned early on. A filthy night, almost blowing a gale, the forecast had said sleet, no way, it was very wet sloppy snow. I had considered the cape and leggings, but in such a wind I had learned the hard way, a cape acted as a sail, alright when you were going with the wind, but sheer hell when it was against you. I used the cape as further waterproofing for all my parcels. Even so, at times, standing on the pedals in the lowest gear of my three speed the wind held me stationary until the gust died and I could make a little more slow headway. I had biked the fourteen or so miles to Smeeton, with orders for... two wool blankets, four pairs of pit boots, two pairs of ladies' slippers, three ladies' costumes, and two gents' suits. Somehow, I had tied the lot on the bike. Naturally, with all this weight on the carrier and handlebars, the centre of gravity was very high. Any corners were taken erect, or the bike would have shot from beneath me. I had never ever forgotten my first winter at work. I had clocked off at just after six o'clock, went hell for leather down West Gate, banked hard over to turn up Regent Street, never a thought about ice on the road. The bike shot from under me, and almost went through the Thirty Shilling Tailors showroom window opposite, I landed heavily on my left hip. I limped after the bike and picked it up. The left hand crank was bent, it would not rotate. Walked back to the Garage where the 'Ford' foreman almost got it straight again for me with a bending iron. As I walked from the gate at home, Dad was coming back from the lavatory, in the moonlight, he could see the bent crank rotating in its drunken way. He had walked straight over to me, and gave my ear a strong punch.

"I've not bought you the bloody bike for you to wreck," he stormed. Quite a laugh really, my wage was six shillings a week, Mother gave me sixpence back as pocket money, Dad took the sixpence off me till the bike was paid for. Original cost Twelve pounds nineteen shillings and eleven pence. I had as yet not paid a full pound off the bill.

In Smeeton, all very wet and soggy. I started the five or more miles on the round, dropping the orders off one by one as I went on my way, arranging to call back and pick up deposits on the return journey. Not a single item suited, I had to bike the lot back home on a still wet and stormy night. Believe it or not, the worse memory was repacking the parcels on either some none to clean tables, or even on the floor.

This had decided me look at the financial situation. The R.A.F. had 'given'? me just over thirty three pounds on demobilisation. Mum had saved the shilling a day allowance the R.AF. had arranged for me, but I still needed to save up to buy an old banger motor. A nineteen twenty eight Morris eight horsepower, four door, four seater, became available. It used all I had in the world, a life's savings, one hundred pounds, and then I had to slave for many a Sunday getting it road worthy and pristine. (The spare wheel turned out to be a worn out tyre on a wheel full of grass) The last work was a hand paint job, finished off with a clear varnish top coat, till all was ready to start work on the next Friday night, all gleaming, in Cobalt blue with black mudguards. My pride and joy. After about an hour's work, I came out of a house to find a group of five or six small children, jumping on the running board, running up the front mud guard, stepping up on to the bonnet, then up on to the roof, running across the fabric roof and jumping down to do the circuit again. I almost went spare, caught the last in line, cuffed him round the ear and threatened all with the same, if! Two calls later I drove back to the end of the street. All of them were lined up waiting to bombard my little car with almost half a building brick each. I had no alternative, revved, changed down, and charged towards them. At the last moment they all dropped their bricks, turned tail, and ran.

Chapter 3
Right Back In At The Deep End

All that was now was some considerable time ago now. I had done well, and the firm were well pleased with me. So much so, that they had hired a team of canvassers on territory nearer home, and provided me with enough customers to start a completely new journey. I had needed to ask directions in the street from an attractive lady. During our conversation she had asked what I did, and as a result of telling her, here I was, in her kitchen, fancying her like crazy, and still watching, 'that button'.

She really did attract me, her clean walnut brown wavy hair shone with health and care, the smile was sort of special, almost mocking in a way, her clothing was worn, but well cared for, very good legs, and that bust was one worth dying for. I had always been a breast man, but with legs like that, it was all a bonus. Not at all a sensible outlook, I had been told often enough, 'don't get involved', once you have bitten the cherry, who is going to pay the bill, not her, you're saddled'.

But, that fourth button was still hanging on. Her brown eyes watched my discomfort with amused interest. The look almost said to me. 'Make a pass if you dare.' Looking back I now realise I really was considering doing so.

"Do you carry skirts and blouses?" she asked.

"Sure, just give me a moment." I shot out of the door, up the steps, back to the street above and my car. Keys in my hand poised ready. Back in a few minutes with three boxes balanced on one arm, I was struggling with the door knob, she let me in. "Three boxes?" Her eyes raised the question.

"I have brought jumpers as well, it's almost autumn."

"Good thinking," she nodded her approval.

"I have brought thirty six bust and thirty eight hip, is that about right?

Hoping I had not left any labels on to show they were in fact thirty eight bust and forty hip.

"If you say so," she countered, "a real salesman I think, I had better keep my eyes on you."

"Can I keep mine on you while you do?" Was my swift response before I had realised. "Sorry, that slipped out."

"I bet that's the only time you swear?" Eyes watching me, so full of innocence. I really was nonplussed.

Did she mean what I thought she meant, or was she naive? I stood blushing whilst she sorted through my boxes. She removed garment after garment, holding some against herself, discarding others, I looked around. As usual in this district (a colliery village) a huge fire was roaring away in a kitchen range. The black leaded metal gleamed, the burnished steel parts reflected the flickering flames. The oven handle shone with regular use, not a trace of ash in the clean hearth. A plain worn table in the centre, covered with a green chenille table cloth. At the corners and table edge it was almost worn through with constant use. Four kitchen chairs that had once been painted, were now showing plain wood in parts with constant handling. On the right of the door I had just come through was an old fashioned glazed clay

16

kitchen sink, showing obvious signs of many years use. Above it there was a window, both halves of which were almost fully open. I had to grin to himself. A huge fire, then an open window to let the heat out, Typical collier's, their nineteen hundred weights of concessionary coal per month had to be burned. To the left of the sink and window, appeared to be a long low table, it went right up to the far wall, it was also covered with a cloth, well worn again, but clean. My eyes then swivelled to the far corner, another door. Then I spotted her reflection in the huge mirror over the fire. With a skirt held to her waist and a jumper to her chest, she was supposed to be looking at her reflection, but, she was watching me. We were both a little startled at being so caught out. She sorted, swapped, sorted again, then turned with a note of finality, three skirts, a jumper, and two blouses over her arm.

"I can try these on?" It was more of a statement than a question. She rushed through the far door, and I heard her feet pounding on a staircase, without awaiting my reply.

Deep in thought I began to put the left garments back in their respective boxes, I had not felt so enamoured about a lady since my callow teenage years, I again realised they were dangerous thoughts, so often I had been warned. 'Don't get involved, one slip up and who's going to pay? Not them for certain.' I thought, nay hoped, she was not that sort, but who was to know these days. To get away with it, they have to be good at it. I remembered an old lady inviting me in last year, all on her own. I had suggested she should have a friend or neighbour present. "Nay lad, I can see tha's honest, come on in."

Laughing, I had explained to her. "Burglars and wrong doers always look respectable, they don't go around in masks wearing striped jerseys, like you see in cartoons."

"Well, if tha tries owt, tha'll get a flat iron round your ear," she had promised, laughing fit to burst.

No doubt I really did fancy this one, what, if anything, did she feel about me?

A flurry of footsteps and she was back in the kitchen with me, swiftly bringing to an end my lurid thoughts. A vision, pleated skirt, tight jumper, sheer stockings, and high heeled shoes. My erotic thoughts returned, slight makeup had also been applied. She did a twirl for my inspection.

"Like it?" she questioned.

"Boy do I?" I almost gasped. No bra for sure, you could have hung your hat on those nipples. Light then dawned, she had not brought any of the other garments back down with her. Doubts assailed me. "W W What about the others?" I hesitatingly asked.

"Oh, I am keeping all those anyway, I just thought I would ask your opinion on these. She laughed, no doubt at my obvious discomfort, and ran back upstairs. Realisation hit me, I began to worry even more, new customers were limited to twenty pounds worth of goods until they had proved themselves. She had taken over twice that amount upstairs. All those warnings, all the hard cases in Smeeton I had coped with, and now a tight blouse with worn button holes had trapped me. Sweating with worry, I began to repack my boxes.

She was back, a bundle of price tickets in one hand, the other, clutching I knew not what. Again dressed in the original skirt and blouse, but now every button but the top one firmly fastened. I really did feel physically sick.

"You do take a shilling in the pound weekly payments?" She asked the question all bright and bubbly, not a care in the world. My spirits dropped yet another notch.

A resigned "yes of course" escaped me.

"Well give me a receipt for this," handing me the bundle, "that will leave a balance of nine pounds ten shillings, you can book that and I will pay you ten shillings a week." I sorted through the bundle of treasury notes, she was right. I could have kissed her with relief, but not after a scare like that.

With trembling fingers I began to make her a pass book out, "I er do not know your name."

"Linda Briggs, Twelve Bugby Road, you do know the name of the village?" That comment was full of sarcasm, but I took it with delight.

"Yes, I'm not that thick, I will put my home phone number on the back of the book in case you need to contact me." That did seem to surprise her, I felt that I had managed to score a point in return.

Not to be outdone she next asked. "I want you to collect on this day at this time, you will be able to find your way, won't you?" The sarcasm surfacing yet again.

"Well if I can't you will have some cheap clothes, but

I wouldn't count on it." Whilst this banter was going on I was trying to balance all my boxes on one arm so that I could open the door with my other hand.

"Put one box on the bath top, I will carry it for you," she instructed. I looked blank. She nodded to the low table in the corner. "Under that cloth is a board, under the board is the bath."

She opened the door to let me through, then with the other box in her hands she followed me out up the steps to the car. I unlocked the door and clambered across the back with my two boxes, she stood back, then muttered. "You need a bigger one."

I withdrew, took the third box from her and answered. "No one has ever yet complained." Complete with my most cheeky of grins. That struck home, at long last her veneer almost cracked, with her cheeks tinged scarlet she turned to go back down the steps.

I drove off with a nonchalant wave to the top half of her body, all I could see as she was disappearing down the steps.

Within less than five hundred yards, the car humming along in top gear I spotted a light on in the back kitchen of one of the houses in the street below. Screeching to a standstill, I leapt out of the car, slammed the door and hurtled down an open 'gennel' towards the house in question. It was the house of a Mrs. Swift, from whom I had never as yet managed to get one single payment since the round had been 'handed over' to me. The kitchen light was still on, curtains still open. Just inside the window a gas cooker, on one of the jets a frying pan full of bubbling tinned tomatoes. A fleeting glance took all this in as I passed the window to knock on the door. Nothing. A quick chassis back to the window, the tomatoes were all but bubbling over the pan edges. Back to the door to really thrash it, then a nip back to the window to watch. "She either answers or has a right bloody mess to clear up" I muttered to myself.

Then it happened... A hand appeared from ground level, groped for the control knob, and turned the gas off. I was really livid, I hammered and hammered on the door with anything and everything I could. Rapped on the kitchen window with a half crown, almost broke the glass, all to no avail. I turned away in disgust, then remembered Super John's comment the one and only time we had ever seen her. "You know Mrs. Swift, your payments are far too slow." Her large protruding eyes, (almost like a Cavalier King Charles spaniel) Her unforgettable breasts. Large and pendulous, when she turned quickly they sort of 'followed her body' in their own time before quivering to a stop in their new position. She had just looked mournfully at us without any change of expression or comment.

Chapter 4
How The Years Have Rolled By

This new round or journey as the firm used to like to call our individual patches totalled five small villages, all basically pit villages, one as a slight deviation still retained a small farming community, a few small factories, and a millionaire fruit farmer. But within two miles was a very active coal mine. So, coal mining was still the main bread winner, even here.

A filthy night, slight drizzle, a touch of frost, with more than a threat of snow. I was cruising home with great care, very deep in thought when I passed a hunched figure walking my side, my way, on the pavement. Wet, tousled, black wavy hair tumbled over his forehead. His fur lined short flying jacket was open to the waist, as I passed I realised the shirt was also open to the waist, no vest, bare flesh bared to the elements. I muttered to myself. "That has got to be Bert," and pulled up on the road side. Got out, and walked back to meet him. "Bert?" I questioned.

"Raff, in't it bloody cold."

We shook hands firmly, me curled up with laughter. "Tha'll never change you silly bugger, why don't you cover your sen up?"

"It's not code enough yet," was his laconic reply. Followed by "It's a long time sin I seed yer, when worrit?"

We haggled for a time, he was sure it was forty four, my guess was forty five. "You had just got back from India," I reminded.

"Course, I was still in India in forty four," his memory buds ticked into place. "You had been issued with wool vests and long johns, thought it was the Arctic you were bound for, I told you it would be India."

Of course he was right, India, the flies, the heat, the stench, the filth, backsheesh wallahs, the runs, and prickly heat all had their airing. Then I remembered to ask about Edna.

"She's alrate youth, she thinks she might be pregnant again, time she were, I've been trying for bloody years."

"You always were trying," I reminded him. "What about your pretty little girl?"

"Little." He almost shouted. "She's fifteen. I'm out most nights sweeping the street clear of randy young lads, be best if you don't see her." That hurt, till the grin on his face proved it all to be leg pull.

"Not at fifteen and a mate's daughter," I assured him.

We went on to discuss work, he was still butchering, I explained I was now a credit draper. "Do you ever get to Warmsworth?" he asked.

"Yes, every Friday night from tea time to bed time, why?"

"I now work for a Warmsworth butcher, he lends me the van to travel, but the council have offered us a council house in Warmsworth, they said next week, but you know councils, leave it for about a month then call. Edna will be tickled pink to see you." It was getting darker, and much colder, we chatted and smoked till both had castanets for teeth.

"I'm off," he suddenly announced, and set off. Over his shoulder he called, "Don't forget to call and see our lass."

I got in the car and started the engine, thoughts and memories tumbling over each other in my mind. I lit up and watched Bert stride off in to the night. Never more than five foot six tall, but broad, now he was very broad. His ever short neck, was now non existent. His head just sat on those broad powerful shoulders. Still the same almost coal black curly hair, with the dark dark eyes all the girls used to fall for. A very good jitterbug dancer, devil may care eyes, frightened of nothing, a good body that could swim like a fish.

Then Edna, sweet adorable innocent little Edna. As pretty as any picture in a pale sort of dainty way. As a young teenager I worshipped the ground she stood on. I used to walk her home the five or so miles after a dance. We held hands almost all the way, then I was allowed a chaste kiss on her cheek, before wending my weary way back. Then she dropped her bombshell, she liked me a lot, but not as much as Bert. He was her true desire. Would I please stop taking her home. We both knew that Bert would never push his attentions without a clear field. So, like a true gentleman, I stood off, and warned all the other lads of the situation. That pretty pretty little girl, prim, immaculate, always superbly turned out, stocking seams and every frill in perfect place was left to catch Bert. I puzzled more, her speech was not like ours, she spoke well, hardly a trace of the local accent we all used. Just how well do they get on? I mused as I engaged bottom gear and moved off through the fresh slick of snow now falling.

More thought, she must be almost three years

24

younger than I, Bert would be almost three years older than I. A biggish gap, but he 'thinks' she might be pregnant, again. "Something must be alright," I thought with a rueful smile.

It must have been two months later, the grip of winter seemed to be almost slackening. In Warmsworth one Friday night, almost an hour in front of my usual time. I was getting to be too early for some of the workers arriving home with their pay packets. No cafe here, no deliveries to pack, just how could I fill in a bit of time. "Edna!" I had lost the bit of paper I had scribbled his expected address, but felt sure that it was eighty eight Victoria Road. I enquired of the next call. "It's a long road at t' back a this one youth," I was informed. Followed by: "Fost few houses are part of t'original village, but they've just extended it, bet there must be two 'undred on 'em nar. Think most on 'em 'ave folk in 'em." With profuse thanks I set off 'round the back.'

I rattled the door knocker above the letter box with some trepidation, stood back and waited for that vision of years long gone.

The door was flung open, a creature stood there, fag hanging out of the corner of her scarlet slash of a mouth. Hair in a mass of plastic curlers, wearing a turban, leaving all the front curlers very much in view. The over long finger nails were if anything, an even brighter scarlet than the lipstick. I was taken aback, and started to stammer an apology for being at the wrong house.

The 'slash' broke into a broad grin and said. "Good God, it's Ron, come on in, cup o' tea, Bert sed you'd be cummin, how are things? Sit yoursen down, cup o' tea and a fag coming up. She almost pushed me into an over soft over worn low easy chair, tumbled cigarettes and matches on to my knee from her apron pocket, and shot through what I assumed was the kitchen door. A running tap and the clatter of cutlery confirmed my thoughts. What few I had left, so different, looks, yes she was a few stone heavier, could well be pregnant, but everything, speech, appearance, hair, nails, make up, so coarse by comparison with that vision I had cherished.

Mouth almost agape I looked round. Everything was worn. Tidy? Well, only just. The walls were almost full of Bert's painting efforts, bare bosomy blondes, woodland scenes, still lifes in a bewildering array. None of your regular bowls of fruit or a cut cheese in this lot. Typical Bert paintings. A tray of empty beer bottles complete with two dirty glasses, an opened packet of cigarettes with a nub end and dead matches in a dirty ashtray. All very good, but just natural talent, no training showed. The dining chair by the door had a tumble of female underwear on it. The next one to it had a pile of ironing completed, on the other side a pile of un finished ironing. The table had a pile of women's magazines and two library books, one opened, and a part finished piece of knitting. She was back, complete with a loaded tea tray, plus a plate of tempting looking home cooked buns.

"Ner me duck, you're looking gob smacked, tell me what you've bin up to. Not married yet Bert ses, not 'as fat as 'im either, an' you still look smart like yer used ter. Maybe I should have had you instead when I had chance."

I looked up at her, still dazed. "You're, you're, so

26

different."

"Someone had to change, we were so different, after a long while trying I realised nothing would ever alter Bert. I was making him miserable, so I did the changing. The things we women do for the man we love." With a mock sigh. Just for a moment I could see the original Edna. She had just finished pouring the tea, we heard the back door open, then it slammed shut.

"Sony me," called out a young female voice, then in she came like a baby whirlwind. Bert's raven black wavy hair, Edna's fair complexion. The sort of figure that 'everyone' dreams of men and women. A real vision.

A moment's hesitation when she saw me, she looked, a little puzzled, then looked at her Mum for some explanation, looked back at me, smiled so sweetly then yelped, no other way to describe it. "It's Uncle Ron." Threw herself on my knee and gave me the kiss I shall remember all of my life. Full on the lips, sensuous, full of anything and everything you like to imagine. Finally she broke away, put a hand on each of my shoulders and pushed herself back to full arms length to appraise me. "He's just like I thought he would be," she tossed over her shoulder to a grinning Mum. "He is better looking than Dad,"

"No way," I managed to protest, "All the girls wanted your Dad.

"Oh! he's O.K. if you like 'em dark, I like blondes like you."

Edna had to laugh out loud. "Meet our Daughter Mae, could you do anything with her?"

Mae shuffled around, sat herself on the arm of my

easy chair and took a firm grip on my right hand. "I've heard about you almost all my life, I don't know who loves you the most, my Mum or my Dad." Edna and I blushed during the few moments silence that followed. Then she was off again, chatter chatter, Mum and I filled in with monosyllables when, if, we got chance.

I glanced at my watch, and with a grunt of exasperation began to struggle to my feet from the over low chair. My 'spare' time had long gone, I was as late now, as I had been early. I could not get out of the house until both had pleaded with me to call again just a soon as I had finished collecting. I drove a few hundred yards and stopped the car at a corner. I could leave it here and walk to collect the few calls I had on the Crescent, its curve would almost bring me back to the car. Bustling around the first corner I was almost knocked for six by a rushing Bert. Dishevelled, a butcher's basket in one hand, an evil looking knife in the other.

"Expecting trouble?" I grinned at him.

"It's all bloody trouble. Customers have complained for years, NO Christmas box, this year we did well, so the boss told me to give pork pies to all the good ones. I did. The ones who got one said we must be making a lot of money to afford it, the ones who didn't are complaining that they should have had one. The knife is for a pack of big dogs that can smell the meat, or the next bugger to upset me."

I had to giggle, he really did look wild. Little old ladies out walking their dogs would have rushed for cover. I told him about our lady village butcher, A very old pensioner had queried the price of a joint. Full of pity, the butcher offered it for considerably less than its true value.

"You're not getting rid of your unwanted stuff on me." She was informed. We both agreed, it was the joys of dealing with the public that stopped us ever getting bored.

I could now tell him I had called and seen Enid and met Mae, plus that I had promised to call back after the toil.

"Smashing youth," from a now grinning Bert. "I shall be just over an hour."

"I shall be longer," I mused trying to calculate mentally just how many more calls I had yet to do.

Eventually, I found my way back to number eighty eight. What a transformation. The table was loaded with a superb high tea, everything had been cleared tidy, and dusted, Enid was wearing a neat little dress, and Mae, she was almost beyond description. Breathtaking was the only word I can use. Her eyes really did shine, the full lips glowed red, yet when she stood on tip toes to give me a kiss of greeting, no trace or taste of lipstick. Her body, so perfect, so firm, yet so yielding as she clung to me for those magic few seconds. I tried to protest about the meal. I was hushed by Edna. "Sit dern and tuck in," were her instructions.

Eating, in spite of all the mouth watering 'goodies' was not easy. So much talk. What about? "Can you remember that time when?" Young Mae hardly made a sound, looking from speaker to speaker, drinking in every word. Lips parted in a sort of expectant way.

At last we had eaten our fill, Edna and Mae cleared

away whilst Bert produced a dozen bottles of the local brew. "Reckon it's been so long we can crack a few?" he grinned.

"Just the one," I protested.

A good hour later a protesting Mae was sent off to bed, the line of empty beer bottles said little for my power's of resistance. The conversation was getting more 'laddy'. Edna made her excuses and left us to it. "I never thought I would ever say such things in front of Edna." I confessed as I realised just how the conversation had drifted.

Bert nodded in understanding, "She is more broadminded now, but she will soon put her foot down if she thinks it's going too far." He motioned me with his head towards the far side of the room away from the stair and kitchen doors. She's still very naive though, I am very lucky. Some years ago we had a rough patch, she wanted me to be posh. It got on my nerves, and I was getting on her nerves, I started calling at the pub for one, then two. Came in for my tea, then back to the pub, darts, dominoes, a beer and a chat without being nagged. One particularly bad winter night, freezing, foggy, I stayed even longer at the pub. The barmaid and I were the only ones left in, she was a good sort, we got on well. Poor lass, her hubby had gone off with a dolly bird years ago. There had been problems with a gang of louts roaming the village late on, would I walk her home? Of course, feeling no pain we set off. When we got to her house she invited me in for a coffee. In I went." He broke off to laugh in an almost embarrassed way. "Daft as it seems now she had no coffee, but she did have a full bottle of Scotch. I woke up in her bed at just after three in the morning. I asked her if she had any chalk. She almost screamed. "What the bloody hell do you want chalk for? we are in enough trouble as it is." She did have some, I got dressed, put the chalk behind my ear and in a very distressed state walked home to face the consequences. Women are funny, when you want them awake they are asleep, when they should be asleep they are awake, she was wide awake. I felt a real heel, sat on the edge of the bed and confessed all. I still can't believe it, but all she said was.

"Don't be silly, you're drunk, you've been playing darts with the lads at the pub, you still have the chalk behind your ear, put it on the dressing table, get undressed and get into bed."

Chapter 5
An Unusual Half Day

When I first started, 'the firm' had a large shop in the big City, but around the time they started my new journey, they obtained a smaller shop in the local town. Not enough room for the mass of furniture and carpets etc that they stocked at the big branch. But amply stocked with our bread and butter run of the mill requirements. Four new travellers, a new manager, complete with office staff, but still with the original supervisor, John.

The manager needs a word. I'm sure it was his first position of authority. His name Bernard Churchill, needless to say it was beyond our place to call him Bernard, but behind his back I always called him Winston. Very tall, some would say 'spare', I say thin. Sparse greying hair, with a terrible dress sense, his regular outfit was a suit in a peculiar blue. Not as dark as navy not as light as sky, somewhere in between. It had a firm chalk stripe about one and a half inches wide, and in between the main stripes it had about five fainter stripes. His trousers were three to four inches too short, very bright socks, and to ruin it all he favoured a mid tan shoe. Invariably, patterned shirts, with bright eye damaging patterned ties. Even now, I shudder as I recall the memory to write. For all that, in his way, he was fair. When on unsure ground he stuttered, when he felt on safe ground he was a different man, all together. I could cope with him, BUT! He had 'set on' his own P.A., secretary, personal assistant, call her what you will. Her hair was the brightest red I have ever seen on a woman, suppose it was pretty hair really, but some of the various styles she arrived in were beyond belief. A mass of ringlets one day, piled high on top another, her dress was always (in her view) the very latest fashion, my big dislike however was the mass of perfume she used. She must have put it on like a navvy douses his chips with vinegar. Finally, she was bossy, and always right. Don't have any doubts, she was never ever in the wrong

Thursday, one thirty p.m., half day, a glorious day, I did not have a care in the world. It had been a good week, almost double my normal takings, three new customers had paid very good deposits. Hardly a one had missed paying. then the main reason that I was 'On top of the world.' 'She' had not found a single thing wrong with my ledgers. For the first time in ages, 'Fussy Breeches' as I delighted in calling her, could find no fault. I felt the need of a mild celebration. No steady girl friend, too busy, very long hours. When you arranged to meet a girl they expected you to be on time. Not hours late with the usual, "Very sorry I was held up at work."

Half days 'should' start about one p.m. but it was usually after five, chasing back orders, doing urgent deliveries, getting out more goods on 'appro' for the next weeks work. I went home and had a proper lunch with Mum, she did me what she used to call. 'The washday meal', one of my favourites. Cold roast pork with fried mashed potatoes and pickled cabbage. We laughed when she reminded me that as a child I had once asked. "Why can't you wash every day, Mam?"

Then for the first time in ages I had time and the

desire to take the dog a walk. Dog!? she was almost human, I swear that she understood every word that you said to her. Dad had an old 14/18 army pal that managed a farm on the 'Moss' near Southport. Poor Bill had fallen and damaged his back. No longer any use on the farm, the owner had sacked him, a tied cottage, so no work meant no home. Southport council had allocated him a house, but the rule was. NO DOGS!

He had written Dad to explain all this and finished up by saying. "I shall shoot Scamp on Sunday and we flit on Monday. I will let you have the full address when we are settled." Dad sent a telegram, "Don't shoot, we will collect Sunday."

Amusing in a macabre sort of way, Dad had fallen on his 'already' damaged back and could not face the drive, so I had to do the driving for him. So had started what proved to be a very long and loving dog man relationship. She was never ever on the lead, her nose was always an inch off your leg. You went in a shop, without instruction she sat outside and waited, if you met someone in the street to chat, she just sat. Mum kept her 'everyday' coats on a peg at the foot of the stairs. One, an old one for fetching the coal in, another, slightly better for shopping. Scamp would be asleep on the hearth in the room. If Mum put her foot on the bottom step to go upstairs or get the coal coat, nothing happened, but if she took the shopping coat the dog was at the front door before her. All dog people have had a 'special', this was ours, a very special friend.

She had one possible fault, rabbits, she would catch one, start at the head and eat the lot, the next day the stench from her 'wind' was almost unbearable. A farm dog yes, but what sort? Certainly some bull terrier, a lot of collie, what else is wide open. Too solid and strong for any other dog to offer a fight, a warning curl of the lip and a muttered growl was all they needed telling.

I went down the long cold stone passage, old oak open stairs on the left, the large stone pantry down two steps on the right, through a little door at the end into a lean to kitchen. The sink was facing me, behind it a window, the ceiling so low no one could stand erect to wash or shave. But no Mum. I went out through the back door on the left and looked across the large yard. Years ago it used to be a farm crew yard, still no Mum, so I put the car away, called Scamp and set off through the front door. Down Burns Lane and to Assarts farm, left across the river, up the hill to the pit, across the pit yard up to the forest, turned left and came out at the top of Putney Hill. Beneath me spread the village of my birth, it felt good, the first time in ages I had been up here. I walked back in home to be met with:

"Where have you been? I've been looking all over for you."

"Been a walk, I was looking to tell you but couldn't find you."

"I must have been in next door."

Time for no more comment, next door was our tartar of a landlady. The original piece of nasty work. Widow of a former police sergeant, she almost spent all of her life secreted behind her heavy curtains minding 'other' peoples' business for them. We did not neighbour at all, for Mum to have been in there it must be for something

35

special, not for my ears.

"I think I will go to the Hare and have half an hour with the lads," I proffered.

"You won't be seeing Maurice will you?" She asked wearing her stern worried look.

"Yes I might, why?"

He seems a nice sort of lad, but I fear he drinks too much. At half past eight this morning he shouted good morning to me and turned in to the Hare and Hounds."

I cracked out laughing. "I've told you what a leg puller he is. I had told him of your fears, ever since he will put the act on just for you. He would just hide round the corner till you were out of sight. No chance of him getting a drink at that time."

"Why the little monkey," she expostulated, but looking very relieved as she said it.

I walked towards the front door, Dad woke with his usual "Is ee in?"

"Yes I'm here, why?"

Yer've had a phone call, frum a woman, she wants yer, urgent."

"Who?"

"I dunno, she nearly got a mouthful after waking me up."

I walked towards the door and sat on one of our second hand worn dining chairs. It was there so that poor Mum could collapse on it after one of her shopping trips. I sat looking round, dare not speak or question. It happened every time, by the phone was a note pad and a jam jar full of pencils. But never a note by Dad. Beyond, Dad's chair, a second hand Berkeley bought when they

36

were first married. It was most comfortable, but no one 'dare' sit in it when he was in. I did when I got chance and many times was catapulted across the hearth when he came in and caught me in it. The other side of the fireplace was Mum's 'lady' chair partner, hardly ever used. It was on the draughty side of the house, no window behind it, so always too dark to read or sew. Poor Mum was always too busy to sit in it anyway, she did everything, cooking, washing up, bringing in the coal, taking out the ashes, darning, mending sewing, pegging rugs. And of course, in her spare time she took in washing. More dolly legs and ponch work with ironing to follow. Still the two irons that were heated on the 'trivet' by the fire. No wonder she was always worn out.

Dad stirred. "It sounded like Winder," he announced and closed his eyes again.

I just sat and wondered, quietly seething. This had been my home since I was a few weeks old. They had started married life in what was known as a 'pit' bungalow. Built for the heroes of W.W.1. to come home to. Dad always said that you had to be a bloody hero to live in one. Built of single brick, four poky little rooms, the only room that had a fireplace was the sitting room. It was in one corner, the one who sat in front of it was grilled, all others risked freezing to death.

Realising there was nothing more to do or say, I tapped my pockets to make sure keys and wallet were with me, let myself (quietly to not risk waking Dad) out of the front door and set off for the Hare & Hounds. I muttering Winder, Winder, to myself till I was level with our back yard gate. Winder, could it have been Linda?

No, she was Mrs. Briggs.

Just in case, I went through the gate and got the car out, set off with alacrity to Bugby Road.

Her door opened almost before I could knock on it, she looked very fetching, hair recently 'done', small amount of make up, a pale blue shirt waister dress that showed her figure to perfection. She welcomed me with what I must describe as a wintry smile. "I expected you earlier than this." The frost was almost thawing.

Dad only gave me a half message, late, I had been out walking the dog.

"How nice for you, why did you not call and take me walking with the dog?"

"It's unusual for me to get a half day and I did not know you wanted to dog walk.

"In any case, it is too late now, children due in seconds, husband in minutes, you will have to call again. I have been 'free' all day."

Winter was rapidly nearing again in her manner.

"What do you want me for?"

"I need to talk to you."

"What about? In any case we can talk now."

"Not when I'm feeding the family, you will have to call again."

We were both silent for a while, then she started again. "You do want more trade don't you?"

"Yes of course, but!"

"No but's about it, if you want it, you will have to call again, but a lot earlier than this." The door was closing firmly in my face. Walking back to the car my head was shaking in disbelief.

"I will never ever understand women," I told myself as I climbed in the car. Climbed in, sorry, it was more 'put it on'. It fitted me like a good overcoat.

So, deep in thought, I drove off slowly, glancing around as I did so. Then, in the row below, I spotted the kitchen door of Mrs. Swift's house was open. "Got her," I pulled into the side, and sprinted down the 'gennel' on tip toes. Shot past the kitchen window, saw no one, then discreetly rapped on the door. Nothing, I raised my hand to try again, but heard a tiny noise. I cocked my head on one side like an inquisitive little puppy. There it was again. A tiny hand appeared round the door edge, trying to pull open the door further. I gave it a slight push to help. It opened a little more. The most pretty (even if filthy dirty) little girl looked up at me. She pushed a filthy little finger up one nostril and lisped. "Me Mamths not in." Then with a valiant attempt, she managed to push the door closed.

Nonplussed, you could say that, no normal adult male could have made any attempt to chastise one so small. "It wasn't her fault, she was acting to orders. I bet that "Me Mam's not in" was the first sentence she had been taught to say." Chastened, I turned away, sick of heart. As I walked back up the hill to the car I turned to look. An unclean bedroom curtain twitched.

The Hare and Hounds red room was unusually quiet when I walked in. Most of the usual crowd were in, but the whole place seemed dead compared to normal. I walked across to the bar thinking, "Just my luck when I needed cheering up." I felt in my pocket for change. "Anybody ready?" I asked the room in general.

"Yer still a jammy bugger," came from Herbert. "Wiv all just bin filled up." Some sort of half hearted calls came across to me. "Hello stranger" "Have you made enough money to afford this week?" "Hi Raff, evening Ron," helped a bit. Joyce, the landlords large daughter greeted me with a smile. "Hello stranger Ron, usual? You've not been in for a few weeks. Her large creamy bust was in it's normal position, resting on the bar. Almost all but the buttons on show. It all lifted as she reached up to get a pint pot off a hook above her head. She supported it herself whilst she pulled me a pint of bitter, took my proffered change, spread it about in the till in its proper place before returning to rest the bosom on the bar again. "Bet it needs some carting about," I thought as I went to a small tub chair by a table in the middle of the room. Wearily I let my body slump into the chair and reached into my pocket for cigarettes and lighter.

"You look buggered, mate," proffered Herbert. "We were just saying we hoped you would come in and liven things up, everybody seems really miserable.

"I really don't think I'm in the mood to help, sorry."

A rheumy old voice spoke out of an equally rheumy old face in the far corner. "It's all the crumpet he gets callin' on these housewives all day, they must be full of frustrations."

"Is that right? Freddy, older, wiser, with a potbelly and a grey moustache asked. "I have heard that yours is the right job to be in for 'spare'."

"I've never had any," I offered.

That really stirred every one up. A chorus of, "Come

40

off it, who do you think you're kidding, a randy bugger like you," filled the bar.

"How old are children when they first learn to speak?" I asked, still thinking of the pretty, filthy little girl.

"I don't know how old women are before they stop nagging," came from the old man in the far corner.

"She has to nag to stop you pestering," came from a grinning Herbert.

"Them as talks about it don't do it," came back as quick as a flash from the old man. "He's the sort that needs watching, all these women all on their own all day, they must be gagging for it."

I took a long drink from my pint and leaned back with a sigh.

"Told you," chortled the old man. "He's had so much today he's buggered."

"I've already said, I've never had any."

"But I bet you've had the chance," from a grinning Fred. "Is it right that it's always on offer?"

"I looked round, unwilling to reply, all eyes were on me, waiting.

"The warnings I had when I started, they owe you money, you bite the cherry, who's going to pay?" The sense of that struck home.

"Any offers?" from a still smiling Herbert. Every body else waited.

"In the early days I had one in Smeeton that had me worried."

Still they all waited. I felt I had to go further. "She was always in a house coat, on a settee at the far side of

41

the room. Book and money on a coffee table by her side. Her constant cry was. "Just knock and walk in, it saves me getting up to open the door."

"What were she like then?" I really had the old man's interest by now.

"A bit mature for me, but a good figure, lathered in make up which always turns me off, I always wondered, what, if anything, she wore under the house coat."

"What happened then?" The old boy was really squirming in his seat.

"Well one day I had obeyed her orders, it was raining cats and dogs, blowing a half gale, I just knocked and went straight in." The room was full of expectancy, I paused to enjoy the tension. "Then I came out a bloody sight quicker than I went in."

"Why?" It was almost a chorus.

I occasionally crossed tracks with a Pearl insurance man, stout, with a navy blue suit and a bowler hat, I would guess his age at fifty something.

His bowler was on the coffee table, his trousers round his ankles, her bare legs stuck out from under him and his backside was going like a weaver's shuttle. I think his backside was covered in pimples, it was a sort of suet colour, but it was moving so fast I'm not sure."

"What did you do?" Herbert was the first with the question.

"I said, I came out pretty fast."

"Come off it, you're having us on again." I shook my head as seriously as I could. But that group of faces was a picture I shall never ever forget.

"What did he do?"

"I don't know, I came out so fast. He did pester me for ages afterwards, pleading with me to not say anything. But I just insisted that I didn't know what he was talking about, I had seen nothing."

"I think he must have moved on to another round soon afterwards, as within a few weeks I never set eyes on him again. You lot are the first ever to hear anything from me." Silence!

Then Fred with a worried look said quietly. "Jeeze, I bet the poor bugger is still having eggs."

"Or she is," with a dirty giggle from the old one. His eyes were shining like a teenager's. "Mi bruther used ter werk for t' Pearl," he announced. "Ee were looking fer new trade, went to this 'erse and said to a little gel "Is yer Muther in the Pearl?"

"Naw, she's in the lavatory, due yer want 'er?"

This all seemed to brighten everyone, all began to air their own experiences, but after half an hour, they quietened, and looked towards me expectantly. I smiled to myself and thought I will put them off with a few of my unsavouries. The first had them almost heaving.

"When they put me on the first journey in Smecton, one call had always been bad, but, for some reason beyond me, I seemed to fit. In no time at all I had the Mum, Dad, and ginger daughter all paying me a pound each. A very worth while call. Of course, there is always a snag. this one was lack of cleanliness, O.K. But! I was 'expected' to drink a mug of tea at every call. I used to sit with the hot mug until I had chance to 'feed' the aspidistra in the front window bottom. One day it was more difficult than usual. Blowsy un clean Mum decided to stop with me to chat."

"You normally drink your tea very quick while it's very hot."

"It's very hot today."

"That aspidistra in the window was always sickly before you started collecting, it looks very well now."

"I talk to it, plants like that." Thinking all the time, I had seen the Mother pick up my filthy dirty mug and wipe it out with a soiled nappy off the floor before pouring my tea in, no way could I face drinking that.

Then a most terrible smell invaded my nostrils, I looked around. Then the Mum did me the biggest favour ever, she toddled off into the kitchen to get the books and money. As quick as a flash I fed the aspidistra, stood, and looked over the settee. A young baby had crawled across the rug, doing its business as it went. Now it was retracing through the mire as it were. I tried to choke back a heave and sat down as the old lass returned."

"Whose is er the baby?" I enquired.

"It's are Lil's, she did a chap a favour about a year ago, she ain't sin 'im since." Thinking I really needed a camera to record the looks on their faces. Flushed with the success of that. I went on. Another wife was idle, dirty, fat and lazy with it. I only ever saw her in a nightdress, low fronted with dirt tide marks all down her chest. The only time I saw them both was when I had missed them Friday night I 'backcalled' Saturday mornings. If I did not call before seven Friday night, they were 'away at the pub', then it was a matter of luck if they had any money left by Saturday morning"

"The front room was bare, apart from a really tatty

44

worn out settee pushed against the back wall. The ash from the fire place could spread at least half way across the room. He was always berating her about the mess. After an average of six months, he took the matter in his own hands, opened the front windows wide, then with a number two collier's shovel, he 'chucked' all the ash out on to the front garden. He then scrubbed all the room, ceiling, walls, and floor till you could have eaten anything anywhere. That was it till a further six months or temper moved him again."

The gang took some assuring, it took serious words before they really believed me.

I finished up with my 'obstacle' course on Fackley Bank. About seven rows of houses built on the bank. They've all been knocked down now and modern houses put up. But then, oh dear. Not a single front door would open (colliery subsidence?) So every one was a back door call. This meant a traipse up each and every long garden path in the dark. Every path was full of rubbish, prams, roller skates, push chairs, rolls of wire netting, barbed wire, you name it. No one did any gardening, most had either a pigeon cote or a pig sty, some both. "My shins are still scarred," I explained as I rolled up a trouser leg as proof.

A serious looking Herbert admitted. I've always reckoned your job to be a doddle, but I reckon I would rather chuck a stint off darn t' pit.

"Have you heard about 'Blossom' from t' Alley?" Queried a grinning Fred. We all waited. Poor Blossom, all knew her, a big gangling lass, well over six feet tall. A couple of sandwiches short of a picnic, yes, but harmless and sweet natured. "She's pregnant," still grinning.

"I don't think that a cause to laugh," I began to chunter. Fred agreed, but then explained why he was amused.

"Her Mum thought she was unwell, and took her to the Doctor. He got her stripped to the waist and began to sound her chest. "Big breaths," he instructed.

"Yeth I know, I've had them thinth I was thiksteen," I eased in my seat, guessing it was a joke coming. How wrong can you be?

Some tests later the Doc. announced the worst, "she is pregnant."

"Cat, well and truly among the pigeons. Mum rushed Blossom back home, searching questions. How or why, I don't know, but in these small villages no one ever says anything, but within minutes, everyone in the village knew. Many searching questions by all the 'do gooders' who flocked around to the house in minutes. The truth came out. Blossom had been selling her body to willing punters at half a crown a time."

Number one do gooder began to scold her. "Why ever did a nice girl like you sell yourself to these horrible men?" Blossom turned to her with spirit.

"Yove no need ter talk, your old man ony gid me one and six..."

It was only a few minutes after nine a.m. when the phone rang. Two six one Chapman speaking."

"My, we are business like this morning," a female voice.

"Who is speaking please?"

"It's me."

"Who is me?"

"Mrs. Briggs," in a very very shirty voice.

"I'm sorry, but voices over the phone are difficult to recognise, that is until one gets very used to hearing them."

"Oh, one must feel very sorry for one then." More like an acid drop in the voice.

I realised it was time to tread on eggs. "I really am very very sorry, but if you would introduce yourself properly it would save an awful lot of misunderstanding and hassle, hello or me is not very enlightening." The phone clicked off. I stood for some seconds, wondering. Had we been cut off? Had she put the phone down in a huff? I had no idea which public call box she was in, nothing I could do.

With a sigh of resignation, I went up the yard to the toilet.

It used to be a midden, a two seater. Full size hole for adults, and a smaller one for little lads like what I used to be. The night soil, men used to come and shovel it all out at some unearthly hour on Thursday mornings. I was never likely to forget. As a little lad I had been taken short in a rush. Just sat down in time when they started to shovel beneath me. All in the dark, not a trace of light anywhere. It had scared me stiff.

However, a few years before the war started, the council men filled it in and fitted us with a water toilet. Better? yes, apart from the fact that it was still almost forty yards 'up the yard', it still had a gap of a foot underneath the door, and over eighteen inches at the top.

Any frost, and all seized solid. It was not the place to sit and read or contemplate your navel. You did what you 'needed', then scurried back indoors. Also, the sewer pipe ran down the side of the path, just where the lorry load of coal parked to deliver our monthly nineteen hundred weights. All that weight had caused a dip in the sewer pipe, so half way 'blockages' was the 'norm'.

I was back in the kitchen, 'stooped' under the low ceiling, washing my hands, the phone rang again. As quickly as possible, I dried my hands and rushed up the passage. It stopped ringing the second before I touched it. I stood looking at it, wondering, when the front door opened and in staggered Mum, absolutely loaded with shopping. Two full shopping baskets, two leather 'bass' bags, all really loaded. She collapsed on the chair beside the door, panting, grey with fatigue.

"Why won't you let me shop for you?" I questioned as I picked it all up and carted it down to the kitchen for her. When I walked back, her breathing was back to almost normal.

"Because you would not do it right." With a weak smile, she hoisted herself to her feet, wiped her eyes and waddled down to the kitchen, then started to bring back in penny numbers all that I had carried down for her.

"Sugar and salt go in this cupboard, bread in the pantry, cheese in the safe in the pantry. I know you try to help lad, but you're more of a hindrance."

She is small of stature, and very overweight, her hair had never had chance to try a perm, but it would not have 'taken' anyway. It was limp and lifeless. Just before her fortieth birthday she had been smitten with sciatica, 'they' said it was now arthritis, she was in constant agony, particularly in her left hip. I still look back and wonder how she coped.

When our old Doctor had called to attend to one of Dad's many pit accidents, she asked if he could do anything for her. He was struggling on two walking sticks, he hated our narrow stairs with only half a foot of tread.

"Woman, if I could cure your aches you don't think I should be hobbling on these two bloody sticks do you?"

The phone rang yet again, with a sigh I walked over and picked it up. "Two six one Chapman speaking."

It was a very irate Linda Briggs, "Are you trying to be stroppy, big, or just bloody difficult?"

"No why?"

"I have already tried to phone twice without an answer, don't you ever try to be awkward or clever with me."

"It has rung once, I was in the kitchen drying my hands, before I could get them dry and pick it up it had stopped ringing."

"I tell you, I have phoned twice."

"Sorry, I must have been up the yard the first time.""

"And what were you doing 'up the yard' as you put it?"

I paused, I could say what I was doing 'up the yard' in one word, but no doubt, that one word would cause ructions.

With great care, as though I was speaking to a young child. I almost spelled it out. "Our toilet is up the yard." It is not right at the far end, but it us the other side of the wash house, the shed, and the coal house, beyond the path Mum hangs her washing out from. I would guess almost forty yards." Silence, whilst she digested that little lot.

"When can I see you? It's getting to be urgent."

"Do you mean like now?"

"Yes, that will do, say fifteen minutes."

"I need longer than that, I have to shave, sort a few orders out, and fill up with petrol. Will you need me for long?"

"That depends on you, I'm waiting," and she rang off.

Whilst shaving I thought long and hard about what I needed to do, how much time I had, the funny ways of women. I must start collecting in under two hours, with luck I could spare her an hour.

Her door opened before I could knock on it.

"Oh do come in kind sir." Over brimming with the sarcasm I was almost getting used to. I let it ride, still consumed with curiosity. As I brushed past her she stroked my cheek with the back of her hand. Checking on the quality of my shave?

"All this is very mysterious," I started. She cut me off in my prime.

"Do you sell good furniture?" The emphasis on good was pronounced.

We do all sorts, it depends what you want to pay.

"It's not for me, it's for my sister, she's older than me. How does she choose it?"

"If it's big it means a run to the big city, smaller items are stocked at our local branch."

"How does she get there?" The fired speech was back.

"I can take her in the car."

"When?"

"Friday mornings are my best time."

"This Friday?"

"If you like."

"Follow me," she turned, slipped on a little jacket that she took off a hook on the back of the door, and scurried out.

I followed, but hesitated about leaving an open door. I was calling to ask, but she forestalled me. "Leave it," she instructed.

Down the garden path, over a low fence, along the top of the garden below, over another fence, then down the side of that garden. Across a little yard and into a door. I stood like tripe. She appeared again and motioned me in.

The kitchen was an exact replica of the one we had just left, apart from the fact that everything was the 'opposite' way round. The kitchen was even hotter than the Sind desert, I was boiled.

An older, very worn edition of Linda fought to get out of a low easy chair.

"Reg," she called out in a tremulous voice. The inner door opened, an old man came in, or was he old? He certainly looked it.

"Yer look like yer Dad, Ron," he started. "I used ter wok under 'im when I fost started at t' pit." Then he grinned. "I 'ope you ant got 'is temper, or can swear like 'im? I almost blushed, I had and did really.

"We need a new three piece, can you help or advise?"

"No, I'm a new boy, but some have been in the city shop since before Pontious got his wings. I will sort 'em out if they don't look after you."

Reg laughed. "Knowing your Dad as I do, you looking so like him, I believe you."

His wife mouthed "Friday morning," to him.
Just as if he had been instructed. "Will next Friday morning suit? I'm on late afters, can you pick us up about half past eight?"

I gulped. "Er um yes," thinking that was a bit early for me

"Can I come with you?" Linda getting in on the act, addressing no one in particular but including all.

I kept quiet, but whilst they agreed, they looked to me for confirmation.

"I don't see why not," but thinking I would have to take everything out of the little car. Stack it all at the side of the stairs, risk Dad's wrath. Plus taking well over half an hour to cart it all in from the yard, and then back out again.

Chapter 6
The First Big Sale

Friday morning, a few minutes before eight thirty, I pulled up with a glow of pride at being on time so early in the day for me. Stifling a yawn, I got out and wended my way towards big sister's front steps. No time, the front door opened, the three filed out. Big sister the last. She dropped the latch, slammed the door, and then looked in her purse to make sure she had the key. Clutching some sort of roll to her bosom, she scurried after the other two.

I asked, "Who wants to sit where?" Linda motioned the other two in to the back seats. "I'm in charge," I thought to myself as I made sure all were in and doors closed firmly.

With my usual smooth take off, I cruised a few yards in second gear, before, with a quick glance over my shoulder, I used a tee junction space to swing the car around in a neat 'U' turn.

"Your car does not jump." From Linda. I looked across at her puzzled. "All other cars I have ever been in sort of jump when they set off."

I thought about it, till light dawned. With a secret little grin I pulled in to the side of the road. A quick glance behind, and I set off again. Too much loud pedal, and not very gentle on the clutch. The little car set off with a jump that would have done credit to any Kangaroo. "Like that?" I asked. She nodded, but I don't think she did.

"Cars are like women, they need handling with great

care and gentleness." Not an answer from any quarter.

I parked the car in the little yard behind the big city shop. Unloaded them, locked it, walked them along the back street, down the side street, then along the main road to the big glass door in the shop front. Pushed it open, and ushered them all in.

The Captain (Men's wear) so called because of his superior military bearing, nodded a respectful "G' Morning Mr. Chapman." I gave an almost salute in return, the 'followers' looked most impressed. The old boy had really gone to town. Everything matched, even his button hole. I pointed them towards furniture, waved towards the senior salesman that they needed looking after, asked to be excused, and headed towards the general office. Knocked and walked in.

Shock of shocks, the only person in there was 'Fussy Breeches.'

She greeted me with a fiendish grin.

"What, what are you doing here?" I questioned.

"We knew you were due here, so we came to keep our eyes on you."

She couldn't, only me and my 'gaggle' knew of this trip. My open mouthed astonishment seemed to please her. "Now that you are here what can I do for you?"

I was some seconds drinking her in. The red hair looked like it was made of cardboard curls, she must have bathed in that perfume this morning. The scent hung in the office like a cloud. Her frou frou skirt stuck out from her waist almost like a ballet dancer's. I began to recover. "Don't whatever you do bend down in that, or we shall all see the promised land." I pleaded. NOT the most diplomatic speech of my life, I realised too late.

"Enough of your cheek, what are you doing here," she bristled.

"I've brought some people in to look at furniture. What's the procedure?"

Her features changed, with a look of fiendish delight she almost spat the words. "You will need a docket signed by the Manager, he is not in, and I'm not expecting him back for ages."

"Well, you can sign me one."

"Can't do it, it's against the rules," she threw at me as she flounced towards a filing cabinet.

"Rules are for the guidance of wise men and the blind obedience of fools." I quoted. "You make it out and sign it p.p. Winston till I can get hold of him."

"Mr. Bernard Churchill would not approve of your flippant manner or disrespect, and you had better not call him Bernard either."

Fuming, I stalked back to my little brood. They were sat on a settee. Big sister was opening the roll she had brought with her.

"What's that?" I questioned as she opened it out. Now I could see it. "Wallpaper," I gasped out loud. "What the hell have you brought that for?"

"To match my settee," said with great pride.

"What with 'fussy breeches', and now this, it was all too much. I turned and fled through the little back door, out to the yard where the car was parked. Lighting a shaky cigarette I prowled round the car, seething, and muttering to myself.

"N.N. Now then M. M. Mister Chapman, upset again

are we?"

I took a deep breath and turned to face the Manager.

"Good morning Mr. Churchill. I guess you could say that, I've brought some new people in to look at a three piece, your bolshie side kick says I've got to have a docket signed by you, you won't be in for ages, she needs throttling does that smelly bitch."

"N.N Now then Mr. Chapman, Y.Y. you must be more respectful to Miss Alcock. You are always rubbing her up the wrong way."

I stifled a grin. "On top of that menace, the people I have brought in have brought a roll of wallpaper to match it. I would have thought that a three piece will outlast over twenty changes of wallpaper."

"The customer is always right," smirked Churchill as he led the way back into the shop. "Guess you were a bit surprised to find myself and Miss Allcock here. It's a new idea. Managers and P.A.'s are to move around different branches on days when travellers are not due in the shops."

I gasped out loud, "The lying bitch said it was because you knew I was due and needed to keep your eye's on me."

"Guess she's winding you up and won that round," he chortled. "We've no real idea of where and what you're all doing really. She does have more trouble with you than any other traveller."

He led the way to the office, picked up a small duplicate book, and turned. "Now, what is the customer's folio number?"

"Not got one, they're new."

"Oh dear, new customers must have a soft goods account first to prove they are good payers."

Already on edge, I blew up. "Of all the bloody stupid ideas. If they want furniture, they are not going to buy something else. They can walk into any other shop and be welcomed with open arms. Do I now say sorry and take them back home?" I was short of breath, but not finished yet. "It would have been a bloody good idea to tell me of these silly bloody rules before I made myself look such a bloody prat."

"B.B.Bu." he started. "I. I. I think we can w.w.waive the rules as these are special circumstances."

"What's so bloody special about somebody wanting to buy what they want?" I stormed on.

He was recovering fast. "H.How much do they want the docket making out for?"

That finished me off, I really blew. "How the bloody hell do I or anyone else know that till we know what they want? Make a flaming blank out and fill it in after, if ever we do make a sale."

Then he realised he was a manager. "I. I. do not like your tone or manner, kindly remember to whom you are speaking."

I had had enough, I turned and stormed back to my little group. They all still sat in a huddle, looking petrified, they must have heard my outburst. The wallpaper roll open on the settee seat. The colours really shrieked at each other. I rolled it up and asked. "How often do you decorate?"

"Twice a year with our big coal fires," Reg proffered.

"How long do expect a three piece suite to last?"

The "years and bloody years I hope," escaped from Reg's lips in a heartfelt voice.

"Forget this," I instructed, just look for a suite you like whilst I hope and pray for us."

Reg muttered something like "That's the first good sense I've heard in weeks." Then almost choked on the words when he saw his wife's face.

The women went to join the unsure, hovering, salesman. Reg held me back, muttered in my ear. "They've only borrowed this one roll from the bloody shop." With a conspiratorial grin and a wink he scurried after his boss.

I must admit that made me feel a whole lot better.

We were a joyful bunch as we gathered around the car almost an hour later. 'They' were happy, the suite they picked had a fade mark along the back, a considerable discount, and the fade would not be seen in it's 'back to the wall' situation. I was grinning as Reg had produced a roll of notes and paid cash, the pair and their 'dockets', could take a running jump.

"How about a celebration cup of tea?" I suggested.

"Thanks, but no thanks," from Reg. "First time in the big City for years, I'm on late afters, so there's no rush. We can cum back on t' buzz, an' I can get a dinner in t' canteen. Y'ar like yer Dad, I thought you were going to peel him one off." Arm in arm, the pair of them poddled off in the direction of M.& S.

"How about you?" I asked Linda.

"Yes if you're not still in a temper."

"I soon back off when the others see sense," I admitted.

A clean cosy cafe on the corner tempted. Table cloths, a good cup, and a home made scone each helped the mood. "How long before you start work?" she asked

I looked at my watch and calculated, the journey back, dropping her off some miles beyond home, then back to re load the car, before I could start in earnest. "Must start in under two hours," I explained.

"Can we stop some where and talk?"

"Here now, warm, cosy, good tea."

"No I mean somewhere, alone." I gave her a sidelong glance. No expression at all, she gave nothing away.

"I thought the talk must have been about a suite for your sister."

Her head shook. "I need to tell you, ask you, awe it doesn't matter."

"With a puzzled sigh, I got up and led the way out, she followed, then tucked her arm in mine. I made to break away, but she clung on. "We are together," was her explanation.

The little car buzzed happily down the 614 at forty miles an hour, she broke the silence with. "Can we stop somewhere?"

With a grin I glanced across. "Layby, fields, or woods?"

"Woods please," She snuggled down in her seat and closed her eyes.

I drove past the Abbey entrance, then took the next right towards the river ford. Turned right again just before it, and pulled up under the trees. "Here do?"

"Can we not walk and sit under the trees?"

I opened the car door, swung my legs out, and

groped under my seat. First out was the trusty ex R.A.F. groundsheet, next a pair of old plimsolls. Her look turned frosty. "I said sit, not lie, and I don't run."

"First my in growing toe nail is giving me gyp, second, the grass will be damp. My Mother is riddled with arthritis. My Dad's Dad committed suicide with it at age sixty, I just hope that it's not heredity." I stood waiting, she got the message and swung her body out of the car, then stood up. I motioned that she should shut her door, then leaned through the car to drop her door catch, locked my door, pocketed the key, waited.

"That ground sheet looks too handy to me." With doubt in her voice.

"Car repairs and punctures," I explained briefly. Then went on. "Grovelling under a car without any protection can ruin suits and health." We set off in what can only be described as an 'uncomfortable silence.'

However within a few hundred yards she nodded towards sloping grass under a large oak tree. I spread the ground sheet, sat on it, leaning against the trunk, she sort of folded her legs underneath, and sank down on them. I lit a cigarette and waited, wondering what was coming. A grey squirrel scrambled down, and squatted in the vee of a low branch. It sat there in the classic squirrel pose, tail curled up its back, nibbling 'whatever' in its front paws. I shuffled over to her, nudged her, and whispered. "Look along my finger."

She did, and smiled with pleasure. "What is it? It's pretty."

I looked in disbelief, "A grey squirrel, you've seen one before?"

"Only in a zoo."

"I thought you walked."

"I do."

"Well keep your eyes open, only people who look can see."

"You're different to other people, your mind works in a different way. You even see and say things differently." She wriggled herself into a lying position. The squirrel moved, and leapt from branch to branch through the trees. "It's so agile," she murmured. As she watched it intently.

"Chip, chip," pause, "chip". Motioning her to be quiet, I stubbed my cigarette out on the tree root, slowly got to my feet, eyes aloft, I moved quietly away, listening with great care, trying to get the sound direction right.

Eyes searching the branches above, I crept slowly and quietly, step by step. Suddenly, the most painful stab in my foot, I let out almost a howl.

"What's up," she asked.

"Dunno," I held the pained foot off the ground, almost two feet of old wooden plank was stuck to it. Using my foot as a fulcrum, I levered the plank away. Almost two inches of rusty nail, already bloody came into view. "Bloody army's leavings," I swore, and in temper, 'wanged' the nail in the nearby tree trunk. I looked at it again, beginning to think more clearly. "That's a lethal weapon, I will take it home and bin it before it cripples some child."

Hopping back to the groundsheet, I sat and eased my plimsoll off to expose an already bloody sock. Then with great care, eased my sock off. I twisted around to try and see underneath my foot. This way, that way. No way could I see it.

"Let me look," she offered, and bent my foot back.

"Ouch."

"Sorry."

I rolled on my back, all she said was. "It's a big hole." Then produced a silly little bit of lace to dab at it.

I rolled to my left and fished the car keys from my right trouser pocket, handed them over and instructed.

"There's a clean piece of white cotton cloth in the driver's door pocket, and a bottle of water under my seat. Will you please fetch them for me?"

"But I don't know how to unlock a car door," she wailed.

"You put the bloody key in the key hole and turn it," I snarled in return. As she went I reached over and again removed the weapon from the tree trunk, as I feared the nail was almost rusted through. "In growing toe nail on one foot, gangrene in the other, I've got to learn to limp with both feet." I was chuntering to myself as she returned.

"Put your foot in my hand," she instructed. I almost grinned as memory stirred.

"That's not a foot."

"Oh don't let's quarrel about half an inch." But now was not the time. Nor did I know if her sense of humour was up to it.

She insisted on doing the foot washing, and was very gentle with me. She had also brought a piece of old towel from under the seat to dry with. I did not have the heart to tell her it was what I used to dry the dog's feet on.

62

"Do you like having my foot in your hand?" Produced nothing other than a comment.

"Your feet do not smell."

"If your feet smell and your nose runs, you must be upside down." I tried. But she was busy trying to separate my toes to dry in between.

"I would rather do that myself please."

"No I... Your toes are all webbed," she gasped as I gently did the best I could between them, from above and below.

"Yes, the hospital has tried twice to separate them, they just heal up, and are very painful till they do. It's best to leave well alone."

"Your big toe is bent."

"I know, when I was about ten years old they bought me a pair of good brogue shoes. They were so 'special' I was only allowed to wear them on very high and holidays. When they were too small for me I had to keep wearing them as they were still as good as new."

I bound the foot as best I could with my clean pristine 'spare' hanky always carried, then eased the foot gently back in it's plimsoll without a sock. Looked at my watch. The spare time I did have, was all but gone. .

Then I heard it again. "Chip, Chip". I looked aloft again, searching. There it was. Almost directly above. I motioned her to me and pointed.

Tail wedged against the tree trunk, it was searching in the bark for insects. It looked down at us, showing all its colours.

"There are no birds here with such colour," she muttered. "Where's it come from?"

63

"It's a native, greater spotted woodpecker, I was expecting to see a green."

"You're pulling my leg." As it flew off to a safer area.

I was going to start explaining, when the expected 'Green' chipped and flew off almost on the same line. Laughing as it went.

As I hobbled and she carried, back to the car I explained. "The old folk call the green the rain bird, when it laughs, it's going to rain."

"You did see it?" I questioned.

"See what?" she asked. Followed by "I don't want today to ever end."

In silence, I loaded my bits back where they belonged, plus the offending plank, and climbed in.

As I put the key in the ignition, the first large spots of rain spattered on to the windscreen.

"The green one was right then."

I sighed, started the engine, and drove off.

Chapter 7
An Unusual Favour

I was not a happy lad on the Saturday morning. In spite of a good soaking in salt water, liberal applications of antiseptic, and an assortment of plasters, both feet were in agony. Last night's 'round' had been diabolical. Apart from the feet pain, a mass of customer's had not been in, loads had missed paying. Takings were right down. Some, that had still been in had met me with. "Yer'll 'ave ter give us a miss this wik youth."

"Why does it all come together?" I moaned as I hobbled towards the harshly ringing phone. Then half smiled as I realised the sight I must have been as I did in fact limp with both feet.

"Two six one Chapman speaking," I almost barked into the instrument, it was all almost lost in the clatter of falling coins as the pay phone button 'B' was pressed.

"Good Morning Uncle Ron, it's Mae from Warmsworth."

"Oh, hello Mae," in a half hearted voice.

"Can you bring me some frocks next Friday?"

"Yes, anything special?"

"No, you will know best, sorry, in a rush, must go, see you next Friday." The phone just burred at me. I put my end down, opened my note book, deliberated, then just wrote Mae. Frocks, she would look stunning in a sack.

Before I could move, it rang again. "Sorry mate, give us a miss this week, Co-op quarter ending." The phone went dead, now I knew why, but I did not know who had phoned.

With a big big sigh, I put the receiver down and hobbled into the kitchen to doctor my feet again. The 'nailed' one was a sort of purple orange, the other, a peculiar squishy white. I thought a while, then said out loud. "Iodine", and daubed a liberal mass of the stuff all over both feet. When I next removed my socks they were full of 'strings of skin'. Both still tender, but they looked and felt much better. Both short of a top layer of skin, Wonder if they stock cotton socks at the shop? Apart from, then someone can bless them, they will be more gentle than my normal rough wool ones.

By Friday, complete with cotton socks, 'things' were a little better. Of cause the collections had suffered. There would be no commission earned this week, just the basic wage. Even Reg's cash three piece had not made up enough takings. Just hope that this new week starting would be better.

I pulled up outside Bert's house, and put a half dozen dresses in a suitcase. My competitors did not bother, they just threw them over an arm and let the world see. I felt that some, if not all appreciated my actions. I set off down the path towards the front door. It opened, and out rushed an excited Mae. "Did you remember?" She was almost gasping.

"Remember what?" Enid's stern voice from her rear.

"I phoned Uncle Ron and asked him to bring some frocks," a crestfallen Mae admitted.

"Without my say so? I said I would think about it."

I just turned and took the case back to the car. Then returned empty handed. "You, you, said, you promised," bottom lip beginning to tremble.

My arm went round her now shaking shoulders.

"You should not have asked without permission," I admonished. "You're a big girl now, and cost more than you used to, their income is not high, all spending must be planned. Doing a silly thing like that deserves you being taught a lesson." Now the tears really came, she shrugged out of my grasp, ran in, and upstairs.

"Thanks for your support Ron," Edna looked a little wistful, but smiling. Looping her arm in mine she led me indoors. "She really must learn the hard way though. Can I trouble you to bring them again next week?"

"Of course, if you really want me to." I was worried if I was doing right.

"She really needs a lot of new clothes. Her 'boobs' are growing so fast she is busting out of all she has. I was going to ask you tonight anyway, but jumping the gun like that she has to be taught. We are going out next week, so you will have to put up with her on her own. Will you be able to cope with her?" I did not notice her quizzical look.

"If the price is right, I can manage two, if not it will be the one only."

"Say a total of ten?" I suggested. She was quietly thinking about that. So I added. "Leave it with me eh?"

She nodded with relief...

Next Friday, almost without a care in the world, I sauntered up the garden path again, complete with my full suitcase. Again, the front door was flung open by an excited young lady. "Did you?"

"Yes, have you been a good girl?"

"Ever so ever so," she literally dragged me in, shut the door, and dropped the latch!

"Off you go to your room," I instructed, as I handed her the case.

"Tea mashed on table," she flung over her rapidly disappearing shoulder. I poured myself a cup, added my one tea spoon of sugar, stirred and sat down on the low settee. As I got out the cigarettes and lighter I glanced down, the local paper was inviting. No time! she was back.

The dress she nearly had on had given me food for thought. But Miss Cookson at the shop had modelled it for me. With its draw string neck tightened to one side, the bow hanging on the shoulder, it had looked very chic. Not any more, the 'draw string' was nowhere to be seen. The neck was low, very low. Her 'buttons' were only just holding her boobs in. Certainly no to a fifteen year old, and no no no to Edna's daughter. I shook my head and announced, "No way."

Pouting her disappointment, she shot back upstairs. In less time than it takes to tell she was back. "Very very nice," I approved.

"But it makes me look like a little girl."

I struggled to my feet and instructed, "Come here." She came like a well trained puppy.

"Will you please take notice of an older man?"

"You're not old, you're in your prime." She seemed somehow more bold now.

"Thanks for those kind words, but will you listen to what I say?"

"Of you, yes of course."

"You are a very attractive young lady." I started

"You really think so?"

"I know so, but we do not keep such stunning looks for long enough. The biggest mistake your age group ever makes is putting it all on show just as soon as you find out that you've got it. You all try to be older than you are. Nice boys will be frightened of it, the only ones attracted by it are the ones that you are better off not knowing. Please try and keep that little girl look as long as you possibly can. You will be glad that you did in the long run."

"I know who I want now," she breathed up at me. Her large brown eyes were almost luminous as she gazed at me with adoration.

"You might think so, but you have years yet to change your mind." Somewhere in the back of my mind, alarm bells were ringing. I realised that I was sweating. "I really mean that," I sort of croaked at her. "I must be going soon, off you go and try the others on."

I was now sat on the very edge of the settee, uncomfortable and unsure. She had four frocks hung on the picture rail in the front hall. Room door left open. For the last two 'changes', she had not bothered to go upstairs or close the door. I had protested, but my comments only produced...

A look with lowered eyes, a coy smile, and the comment. "It's only you Uncle Ron, I'm safe with you, aren't I?" No doubt she had a stunning body, in nought but bra and pants, a sight for sore eyes. But!

I needed to ponder. "Why should I be different? Does she think that I'm made of stone? My sweaty clothes were sticking to me. I tried my best to produce a nonchalant grin, urged her to hurry, reminded that I had more calls to do.

We eventually agreed on two garments, well within Edna's budget. I was feeling a little less uptight when she took all upstairs again to pack the case with 'unwanteds'.

However, when she came back with the full case, all she had on was a house coat. NOT FASTENED!!!!

Before I could get up, she was beside me on the settee. Then with that female voice that they can all use when they want, she spoke.

"Uncle Ron."

"Yes,"

"Would you do me a great big favour?"

"Of course, if I can."

"Oh, you can," in a very sure if breathy voice. "You know that I am still a virgin?"

"Good God, I should hope so at your age."

"I'm the only one in my class at school that is."

"Don't believe them, they are trying it on to look big, whilst actually making themselves small and cheap."

"My best friend lost hers last week, she says it was all a disaster and a real mess. She told her big sister, who told her off and said she should have got a man that knows what he's doing instead of a boy."

"Her sister did not tell her off for doing it then?" Very bemused.

"No, just that she should have got herself a man." The last comment after a pause for thought. I could feel sweat trickling down my ribs. I was well out of my depth.

Mae, apparently unaware of my predicament kept bubbling on as though she was chatting to a school friend. "Now you think that I have only known you recently, but I've known about you, well.... all of my life really. Mum and Dad have always spoke of either Ron or Raff. They both love you to bits." She was sort of going dreamy now, as if very deep in thought she carried on. "Suppose I was in love with you before we met, then when we did, you are even nicer than I expected."

The house coat had opened slightly, it gave a glimpse of a super 'pair', and almost down to the promised land. "Please, I want you to take my virginity now." In one swift movement she was on my knee, arms round my neck, and engulfed me with a real passionate kiss.

My first effort to release myself found a hand on a superb firm breast. I moved it quick, but I still encountered bare flesh. I abandoned all such action, put both hands on the settee seat and pushed us both upright. Now in a standing position, her lips were still glued to mine with the tenacity of a suction pump. We were both panting furiously.

I broke away and managed to gasp. "Be sensible, you're not old enough, your Mum and Dad would kill me, we are almost life long friends." Frantically trying to think of all the reasons why I should not.

"None of my friends are sixteen, Queen Victoria is dead you know, and I was not thinking of telling Mum and Dad."

"Mae, please, please, please, don't tempt me so. I do

71

thank you. I really am grateful. You're so desirable, yes I want, but I just dare not."

I grabbed the suit case, took seconds to scrabble with the door latch, and fled to the car. I literally threw the case on the back seat and scrambled in to my cockpit, but she was already in the passengers seat. Housecoat primly held closed. She looked much older now, very serious. She put one hand on my knee, looked in to my eyes, and said with all the sincerity she could muster. "I mean it, it's you I want, I am sixteen in five weeks time, I can wait that long, think about it and let me know."

Almost primly, she got out, closed the door, holding the house coat closed with two hands she sort of 'swept' back into the house.

I sat for some time, giving my mind and body chance to settle, of all the predicaments to find yourself in. At last I started the engine and moved off. I glanced at the bedroom window and got a glimpse of a forlorn little figure and a finger wave.

Chapter 8
Another One In Trouble

A real disaster of a week, the foray with Mae had made me late, a lot were out, because I was late or because of the Coop quarter ending? My feet were still a bit tender, my mind in a turmoil about Mae, plus the worry if ever Bert or Edna found out.

If possible, Saturday was even worse. What with 'not ins', misses etc, I had finished the round by early afternoon. Then to cap it all, I came out of the last call to find the nearside front tyre as flat as a fart.

I had changed the wheel, looked with worry at the two very worn tyres involved, and was wiping my hands on a rag. (I had not remembered to refill the water bottle!) "Brain dead", I muttered to myself as I squatted again to make sure the work had been completed in a proper fashion.

A modern registration, sixteen hundred c.c. lime green coupe, looking very smart swept into the kerb in front. A lithe fair haired man just over six feet tall eased himself from the driver's seat and came towards me at a sort of nonchalant lope. With a lopsided grin, he asked, "I do hope I am too late to be of any help?"

No mistaking that voice, even if the face and body were less youthful than I remembered. "Eric."

"I knew it would be you, I recognised the squat." We both laughed at the memory. "The last time I saw you, you were almost falling asleep under a Lanchester Ten. It was the day before I joined up.

We had been to the pub at lunch time and had three

swift halves, it was too much for you. Those exhausts really did rust up solid, I reckon that the beer and the struggle had just about knackered you."

By now I was on my feet, we shook hands firmly, whilst grinning broadly we appraised each other. Eric Towser was almost two years older than me, in consequence he had been called up earlier, demobbed earlier. As neither of us had returned to the motor trade we had lost touch. I understood that he had married, worked for the Metal Box Co., and was last heard of in South Africa. Now he was a real lady's man, that loping walk, the lop sided grin, seemed to have all the girls swooning. His nick name at the Garage was. "The Meteorologist." He only had to look at a girl and he could tell weather. Pale brown hair, almost gold in sunlight. The hair so fine it was always flopping over his forehead. His height tended to hide the broad powerful shoulders, his grip was the strongest at the garage. Many times when a petrol tank cap could not be moved, the cry went up. "Has Towser been at this bugger?"

Pale green grey eyes that lit up his whole face when amused, which was frequent, he really had a quirky sense of humour. All in all, a very good mate.

I was looking with envy at his car, almost green with, I said. "It's nice, it's pretty."

"Bloody rubbish," he answered, kicking the rear tyre in disgust. "The prop. shaft 'Hardy Spicers' only last for months, it burns coils out without warning, and it needs a new bulb 'somewhere'every week. Remember about our constant moans in the old days. "It's no use looking good if it don't go.'"

"I bet it pulls the birds though."

"Yes, but when you get one in it there's no room to do any damage. I've threatened to take the passenger seat out to give me more room."

I looked a him with some doubt, his grin gave nothing away, he could be being serious. At times his humour had always had me on edge, did he mean or did he not mean?

"What are you doing now?" Eric's face changed, in a flash he looked very serious.

He thought for a while without reply, then hesitatingly. "Do you mind if I don't answer that one."

"O.K. if that's what you want," I was a little peeved, we had always been so open with each other in the old days.

He thought some more, face creased with worry lines. "No, that's not fair, have you time for a cuppa? I must confide in someone, who better than you?"

"This is coming to the end of a rotten week and day for me, a good idea, where can we go?"

He looked at his watch, deep in thought, looked at it again. Then. "Follow me to my place, she won't be in for two or three hours yet, it's not too far. I will drive slow for you." (A friendly dig at my old banger, no doubt)

He turned his car round, I followed suit, a very sedate drive for about four miles along almost a lane to the outskirts of a village, where he turned into a drive on the right. A very nice bungalow on a slope, the garden on three levels joined by rockeries, pristine lawns, a pond under a weeping willow with a fountain making water music, a garage on the end of the bungalow, then a large double garage further back. I felt a little sick.

"Don't let it all fool you," from Eric as he spotted the look on my face. This lot will cost me five pounds a week plus ten bob rates for the next twenty nine years, Watch out!" He had opened the door and released a bundle of high speed Jack Russell terrier. The short stubby tail just a blur, it did three rapid circuits of the front lawn, paused for a pee, then leapt into the arms of her master.

Mein host produced hot water, a magic potion for cleaning filthy hands for me to 'scrub up', whilst he boiled the kettle, mashed tea, before peering into a large fridge.. "Fancy a sausage sarney?" he questioned.

"Not 'alf, just like the old days eh?" We fitted together just as though we had not been apart for all those years. He passed me a loaf of stone ground whole meal bread for me to slice whilst he popped four huge meaty looking sausages into a frying pan. Within minutes, the sausages were on a plate whilst he dipped the slices of bread into the greasy pan fat.

"I know it's not supposed to be healthy." He started.

"But naughty is still very nice," I finished off for him.

"Who starts?" he asked.

"You do," I mumbled through a very tasty mouthful.

"You're doing credit drapery then?" My eyes opened in surprise. "Watch it, it nearly killed me, if you must, do it for yourself, working for the big boys is a short cut to a nervous breakdown. They will say your takings are short and charge you, they will say that you've stock missing, and charge you. You're already

76

working your balls off for a pittance anyway."

The realisation of the truth of his comments rendered me speechless. "Working for yourself still produces the breakdown, but it takes longer, and you earn more for yourself in the meantime."

My surprise must have got through to him. He had always been so much more 'streetwise' than me.

"We will discuss that later, I must get my tale off woe off my chest before I change my mind." Silence, while we both chewed, drank and thought. Then, almost thinking aloud, he went on. "I've got to tell it all, or you won't understand a thing." He offered cigarettes and poured two more mugs of tea. Put the dirty pots in the sink, sat back, inhaled deeply, and started.

"Most of it happened by accident really, like you, I did not want to go back to the filth. But the first thing I did when I got home was get married. I had to earn, the only work I could get was back to being a mechanic. Started with Jimmy's son who is on his own now. Jaguar agency. Of all the jumped up prats who want a big motor we got the lot. All were bother, the cars and the owners. So I went to a Leyland agency in the big City. An hour's bus ride every night and morning did not suit. The boss wife saw an advert for 'mechanically minded men' at Metal Box. I applied, and got in. The next thing I knew we were in South Africa. I was keeping a production line going every minute of every day. Wogs breaking the machinery, me mending it in all that heat. We were very glad to get back home. The pressures of keeping production going was too much. I had a breakdown. The doctor advised I start fishing again, and have a drink. I now realise he did both to the extreme, I could not afford to.

"One very happy early morning in the top lake at Welbeck I shall never forget. The lake was covered in mist, I hardly caught a thing. But a king fisher came three times, settled on my rod tip, caught three minnows, looked at me with disgust before taking off with them. Then as the mist rolled back the whole herd of over a hundred red deer led by the stag swam over towards me, an awesome sight. But I think that brought me back to reality.

"I got a job with a credit draper. The most mean despicable liar I have ever had the misfortune to meet. I dare not tell you any of the things he did, but he deserves to die a thousand horrible deaths. He had two vans and a car and realised he would get them kept in pristine condition without paying. I finished up by thumping him and walking out. Weeks out of work, then I met a real gentleman. He and his wife had been credit drapers for years, they had had a big round, but ill health caused them both to cut down. Would I go and work for him? I did, like a shot. What a man, fair, honest, we bought together and did the books together for just over a year. Then one morning he just did not wake up. I carried on working for his wife until she went straight on at Kelham Bridge, dropped about ten feet to the riverside. They did not know if the accident had killed her or if she had a heart attack to cause the accident. It was all very sad, I still miss those two wonderful people. The will was read, they had left the business to me and their home to a charity. Naturally it was a big round a lot of hard hard work. But, he had never insisted on customers paying a shilling in the pound. Nearly all new customers were the children of the old customers, so they still paid ten bob a week no matter how much they owed. The children needed furniture, washers, fridges, carpets, all big costly items when they got their new homes, but still paid their regular ten bob. I was working like a slave, a sky high book debt, for the same collections. The bank manager offered me an overdraft facility. But I realised how much he would charge me, and so make matters worse. I really was at my wits end." He reached over to the tea pot, it was empty, he was almost in tears.

I opened my mouth, but shut it when he waved for silence. We both lit further cigarettes. Then after a deep breath he carried on.

"My wife has no interest whatever in the business, no interest in sex or cooking either. She just went to the office, came home at five twenty, put steak, brussels and taters in the pressure cooker for twenty minutes, served it on a plate, put it under the grill, and there it waited for me till ten or eleven o'clock when I got in. Y' know I've never ever had a fresh meal, even Mum used to cook Dad's at three, then put it on a steamer till I got home at half past six. Mind you, it was on a steamer, not under the bloody grill. We had some business friends that used to invite us out for a meal at weekends. Super meals, but she never invited them back. So when I could afford, I took us all to a hotel for a meal as a sort of 'payback'. Of course, that again cost me money that I could ill afford.

She went to choir practice, took part in all the concerts and had a 'hair do' every week. The week of the big show I used to live on fish and chips, pick her up from the theatre and get home after midnight.

Whilst it was all at its worst, a chap from near the County border offered me nineteen shillings in the pound for the lot, book debt and stock. I snatched his hand off. Then I had to try and find work all over again. Not easy. All the firms that tried me were bent to high heaven, the longest I lasted was weeks.

A sort of casual friend who had been made redundant started to call late on Friday nights. He was always telling people how to run their lives, so it must have been a blow to him to be out of work. I think I was the only one he could trust to sign his dole chit without telling anyone. One night he brought the Telegraph to ask about a firm who wanted sales people. I knew them, very bent, so I told him and he went on his way, but he left his paper behind, looking at it, I found it.

Wanted, sales people, car and telephone essential, basic wage ten pounds, commission starting at twenty per cent, rising to forty per cent."

"That's terrific," I butted in. He shut me up with another wave.

"Naturally I applied, got a reply within days." He slowed down and began to speak more deliberately. "The reply told me to report for an interview at nine a.m. the following Saturday morning," he paused, then added, "in Birmingham."

I gasped with horror. "That would mean starting off at five a.m. and not getting lost."

He managed a sickly grin, then added. "I did and I did. The letter head explained that they were suppliers of

80

hearing aids to the hard of hearing."

My mouth opened in terror, we had discussed, oh so often, we were both scared stiff of trying to talk to the deaf. It did not matter how you shouted, they never ever understood what you were saying. We used to have a few customers at the garage that we literally ran from when they appeared.

He knew, he had read my thoughts, he nodded with a knowing half smile. "I sat down straight away to write a 'no thank you' letter, but madam wife would have none of it, at least go and see what it's all about, she insisted."

The next Friday night, the weather forecast was for snow, I set the alarm for four with a secret grin. Woke up, looked outside, we had had almost an inch, but the forecast said it was deeper in the midlands. I rang him at nine to say I was snowed up, the drift in front of the garage door stopped me opening it. He accepted it and gave me the same appointment for the following Saturday. I said forget me, but he liked my letter, felt I was what he was looking for, I had potential, and almost pleaded."

"Did you go?" Knowing the answer would be no, but he surprised me by nodding.

"Got lost in Birmingham of course. It's big, I always did drive on the left, not any more, the approaches to some corners have four lanes of traffic, I 'thought' I needed to be right, but when the traffic cop waved us on, No way dare I try to cross that lot. On my fourth try, he stopped every body, walked across and asked where I wanted to go. I said that I thought I wanted to be over to the right. He said well bugger off, I'm fed up of seeing

81

you. Held everybody while I screeched across them all.

"At nine o' clock I had no idea where I was, I crawled into a phone box, rang him, explained, and pleaded to be let off home. No way, he asked for the number of my box, found out where it was, and phoned back with instructions."

My mind and experience just could not take all this in, it was just not believable. I spluttered, doubted, shook my head. Eric looked on with quiet amusement. He now had the bit between his teeth, he intended to press on regardless.

"By the time I found him, all but he were going home. I'm sure there was only the two of us in these huge offices. He asked questions for almost an hour, I just answered and listened. Then he dropped the bombshell. Next year, all hearing aid dispensers would have to pass qualifying exams to work. The wife was always nagging. 'Why can't I qualify for something?' I must have perked up at this, because he asked, 'why the sudden interest?'

"So, I put all my cards on the table, my fear and hatred of Birmingham, my fear of the deaf, my wife wanting me to qualify, when we did not have the time or money to do so. He assured me that with his training, there would be no problems on any score, and set me on, promising a car as well."

"He's right, I can now communicate with the deaf, they are great people, it's a real delight to be able to help them."

"So what is your bloody problem?" It was all getting beyond me.

"A terrible firm, no principles at all, the end product

or customer satisfaction was of no interest at all. You're taught to use any and every dirty trick in the book to get a sale. If a customer wrote in and asked for you to recall, you never got the message 'in case' it was a complaint. You were never ever allowed to meet any other sales staff. You had office appointments half an hour apart, if ever they slipped up and two were in at the same time, one was hidden in the cellar. No one could win, if you made a call and they were not in. If you left a note you were wrong, or if you did not leave a note you were wrong. They were advertising for new sales staff very week. Any 'doubtful' sales were crossed off your commission until they were very sure, to get to the forty percent rate you had to sell over six aids a week, and they just gave you four leads a week to work with, over half of the leads were a waste anyway. School children doing a thesis, nutters that answered everything that was freepost, folks collecting leaflets, that man really terrified me."

"That I just do not believe," I got in before he could protest.

"S'right, Albert Knight took almost a whole year out of my life, I got him once when he was training me. We were in a town near here. A horrible dirty little old man who had stolen a hearing aid off his dead brother's body, but did not now how to use it. Knight always instructed that he would pretend to read a paper whilst he was listening to your speil, and find fault later. The little old man asked. 'What's ee doin' ere?' I replied. "I'm training him." It's a good job the old chap was quite deaf and did not hear his exclamation.

I liked that one, and had a little chuckle. Then thinking, I asked. "But how do you get the deaf to understand you ?"

"It's easy with training, you must not shout, but you sort of project your voice. Mind you you've a sore throat for some weeks before you master it. It feels as though you've got a squirrel's throat full of nuts till you do.

Anyway, one Saturday morning I rounded on him, told him I could take no more, I could not stand the attitude, the principle, always replacing people etc. He promised me that it was all over, he now had a good team, the size he wanted. From now on all would be different."

"Is it?" I managed to get in.

"Is it bloody hell as like. The following Friday night, Night time Nigel brought his dole chit again, and left the Telegraph again. I browsed, there it was, promising the moon as usual. But below, I spotted another one. 'Hearing aid dispenser's, if you're not happy with your firm, leads, car, treatment, phone Derek on (a London number) You will be glad you did. I did, what a difference, all mates together, christian names, a boozy pub lunch after meetings, better aids, bigger cars. It's hard work, I drive over fifty five thousand a year, long hours, it's often after eleven when I get home, I love the job, the deaf, it really is great being able to help them."

I gave a sigh of frustration, all now seemed to be happy, what really was his problem? I opened my mouth to ask, he forestalled me.

"It's the exam, I've failed once, my last chance comes in just over five months."

"Is it difficult then?"

"It is to me, it's nearly all physics."

"You, have, never, ever, done physics," came quietly, slowly, from my realisation thoughts.

"It is all double Dutch to me," Eric agreed with a sickly grin.

"I am right, you were a Motor Mech in the R.A.F.?"

He nodded.

"I was a wireless mech, group one trade, nineteen months, Cranwell College and all that old boy." (Always have a dig when you can.)

"So what?"

"Wireless and Radar are all based on physics."

It seemed to take ages for this to register, then light dawned. "You still have your notes?"

"Yes, but they'll need finding." A car pulled into the drive, we looked at each other, then he looked at his watch.

"Look at the time, she will be expecting a meal ready."

I muttered something like. "I must be off," and scuttled towards the front door. I had to stand aside as a tall, slim, well dressed women sort of swept in. "It's my fault m'dear, please don't be hard on him, he has real problems." Eric was making a great play of 'pot rattling' in the kitchen as she asked.

"Who was that?"

"A mate from the garage days, I've not seen him since I joined up." He was still rattling pots as I fled.

Chapter 9
Swotting Plus Work Is Hard Going

For many weeks, we were together during every spare moment, in a pub, in a car, at his home, no chance of using my home, Dad would have gone spare. Looking back, I now realise that it was getting us both down, he more than I. His once powerful frame was getting to be almost weedy. He was smoking too much, and I suspected hitting the whisky bottle pretty hard. At his home the greeting was always. "A wee dram mate?" I always refused such an early tipple, we could catch up easily later. At times, we had a little giggle, wondering what other people might be thinking about our keeping such constant company. Otherwise it was a regular solid graft. But one night I realised that at long last it was all beginning to 'sink in'.

The biggest problem I had with him was his lack of understanding of the huge range of sounds that could be heard with a normal healthy ear. The range is so large that a decibel rating needs to be used. Otherwise figures to the power of ten or more are needed. Now he was quoting decibel figures with almost polished certainty. The date of his examination was getting very close.

His employers had managed to get hold of copies of old exam papers, from which I was able to point out that each and every year there had only been one or two questions on any particular topic. Some of the same questions even re appeared after a few years. Between us, we evolved the idea of both answering a question, then comparing our answers. If we agreed, we left well alone, if not we argued and discussed till we got it sorted.

After one long hard session, we had to relax, of course, as usual, the subject invariably finished up on 'the old days'. It was Eric's fault, he had been to help another friend adjust the brakes on his caravan, it was parked on farm land. No matter where he went, friend George always had his trusty old collie dog 'Bob' with him. They had pulled up, opened the boot lid, out jumped old Bob, he stalked to a an electric sheep fence and cocked his leg on it. The poor old chap yelped, jumped back in the car, and spent the rest of the time licking his tassle. When he had finished his yarn, we looked at each other, said "Barrett", and burst out laughing.

During the early war years, the garage boss (Charles E) had started collecting all the second hand car's he could get hold of. No doubt ready to make a killing after the war. All were stored in the old disused garage up on Clumber Street. To say the least, the electric wiring in the old place was suspect. Lead sheathed cables, brass switches and lamp holders, a leaking roof, made you very careful. You never ever dropped a switch without either a 'wiper' in your hand, or an overall covered elbow.

During the wartime shortage of parts, it was a regular thing to go up to Clumber Street to 'cannibalise' for what you needed. A disliked customer, a solicitor named Barrett was a real menace. He owned a nice little fabric bodied one and a half litre Riley roadster, and a horrible mangy lurcher dog. A regular occurrence, Barrett would drive into the centre of the garage, let the dog out, lock the car, and walk off. Whilst the dog would find a poor unsuspecting mechanic lying under a car and pee on him.

On this day, Arthur (the foreman) and we two were all in Clumber Street, hunting for something or other. We all heard the car stop in the yard, heard the door slam, and through the slightly open garage double doors stalked 'the dog'. We all stood up. The lurcher walked past with disdain, no target for him, carried on to the old work bench. (Under which was a transformer) Up went his leg, there was a blue flash, a haze of smoke, a slight smell of roast pork. The hound wriggled at high speed through the part open door (he did not touch either) and was never ever seen again. We agreed, we loved dogs, but not that one.

Eric then went on to tell of a last weeks experience. He had fitted a wealthy old dear in a mental hospital. A very hot day, a severe hearing loss that needed a powerful aid. So it needed a very good fitting ear mould. It did fit very well, so well that the old dear could not get it in. In desperation he had rushed out to his car to get vaseline to help. In his rush he almost fell over a group of nurses listening at the door. Panic over, he packed up to leave, a nurse apologised. She had heard their conversation, gathered others around to listen. It had gone something like..."I do like it so much when you put it in, you can put it in much better than I can, please take it out and put it in again. It's nice, I like it."

Chapter 10
More Old Ground

I had a phone call from an old Smeeton customer, would I please go and see him. Thursday afternoon was not too busy so I went over, called, no one in. I hung around for a while then retired to the Coffee Pot Cafe where all this had started. Nonplussed, I ordered a cup of tea, retired to the rear, and thought, what would it be best to do. I drank the tea, smoked a cigarette, and looked at my watch, I had not as yet used up ten minutes. Dilemma!

A familiar voice from the counter made me look up. "Two cups of tea please, and that haggard old man at the back will pay."

A good old friend, Harold, what a treat to see him, I rushed over to shake his hand. Yet another with a great sense of humour. His happy chuckle always sounded like a well tuned vintage car ticking over. Possibly five eight or nine, broad shoulders, a shock of almost auburn hair, and with a shy cherubic smile. A precision engineer by trade, anything that interested him was done to perfection. If it did not interest, hard lines. I only worked with him twice, once to help him decorate a room, once to decarbonise his car. I had been taught to decarbonise properly, get a hundred percent 'blue' mark on the valve seats. No good to Harold, he had to regrind then re polish with metal polish as well. The walls we decorated, every little blemish was filled, then sanded, polished with a nylon pan scourer, he sized twice, then he put a lining paper horizontal, the finish paper vertical, nary a 'join' showed anywhere. I think fastidious is the best word I can think of.

Seating himself in his shy unobtrusive manner he began to speak.

"Funny seeing you now, I've just seen a really pristine nineteen thirty six Austin 7 Ruby saloon go down the street, it was really purring."

"That brings back a host of memories. Jack Lee and myself had to road test one without a driver's seat. It had gone to be re upholstered. I sat in the back seat operating the pedals, whilst he sat in the front passenger seat, steering and changing gear. It caused a lot of consternation in the market place did that. Their clutch action has never ever been repeated, it all happened in under an eighth of an inch.

Harold chuckled and asked. "Have you seen the blind man's van of late? Remember, he had painted on the side. 'This van is driven by the blind man.' He made window blinds."

"I think I heard that they had stopped him, it worried so many silly people." Thoughts clouded my brain. "Y'know, if every body had to take their test in an Austin seven, there would soon be less accidents."

"Yes, and less people on the road anyway, I reckon only one in twenty would cope with the clutch and lack of brakes. The bowden cables stretched so much, they needed re adjusting every week."

I laughed as I remembered one keen do it yourself motorist. He must have had six cable adjusters on both cables. It looked a real heath robinson effort when you crawled underneath." He joined in the memory, he had fitted no end himself over the years.

All this had my memory buds stirring. Did I ever tell you about the girl friend I had? Her Dad bought one, took no advice, could not drive, guess who he asked to teach him.

"I've got the prize, how did you get on?"

"Rough, it was a real nightmare. He had bought the job lot, car, and garage down the wood side. It was a 'bits fell off a lorry garage', made with four railway sleepers for the corners. The sides were laths and colliery belting, the back just belting, the doors, a frame covered in wriggly tin. Nearly all nailed on with two inch nails, they must have run out of two inch when they got to the back they'd used two inch at the top, but the sides of the back were held on with little short nails only."

"After weeks of taking him out every available hour, I thought he could be trusted to drive it in to the garage himself."

Poor Harold was way ahead of me, he could guess what was coming. He waited with bated breath.

"He stalled the engine twice, so I walked round to take over, no time, he got it started again, let the clutch out, jumped half way in, then jumped straight out through the back. The long nails at the top held, the rest, short ones did not. The whole back opened like a flap, the car scraped through, then the back dropped again."

Harold was helpless, I had to wait before I could carry on. "There's more?" he questioned weakly, drying his running eyes.

"Yes, he was only a little chap, he could not hold the flap high enough for me to reverse it back in. I had to stand, arms aloft, till he managed to jump it back in.

Then I had to do a paint and canvas job on his roof.

"All that to get your leg over?"

"But I didn't."

Recovering, Harold asked if I had known his two uncles, Cyril and Bill. I admitted that I had met Cyril, but not Bill. Cyril was a little fat man, with jam jar bottom specs. Anything and everything worried him. It would take him ages to decide which tools to take with him on his electrical work.

"As different as chalk and cheese," Harold explained, "Cyril was an electrician, Bill a plumber. Bill could do the most marvellous work with hardly any tools at all. If he arrived on the job with a blow lamp and a hammer, the job was as good as done. His 'wiped joints' were a picture to behold."

"They must have both been almost forty years of age, Cyril had always managed on a push bike, but Bill had a love of motorbikes, the bigger, more hairy, the better. His great pride and joy for many a year was a Rudge Special 500 cc solo, which even by today's standards was a potent piece of machinery. It went like a bat out of hell. This was followed by a Brough Superior SS 80."

"They must have had their heads together and realised that a push bike and a hairy motor bike would never ever tempt the fair sex. So they clubbed together and bought a tired old Austin seven, about 1928 vintage. The usual 750cc side valve engine, clutch and brakes you know all about. Sliding overlapping windows fitted to the two doors. The windscreen hinged at the top, so that you could loosen two wing nuts, push the windscreen up, and out. Tighten wing nuts again, and you almost had air conditioning. To open the doors from the inside, a leather covered fine chain went from the door front end to the catch. If reasonable service was given, it all worked rather well. One sunny spring Saturday afternoon, they cleaned and polished everything till it gleamed. Sunday morning, two large gentlemen in brand new suits, one pale grey, one pale blue. Where should they go, that they may find spare popsies?

Gunthorpe Bridge won the vote, and off they went. Within a few miles the sun remembered it was spring, it shone bright and warm. Full of pride Bill loosened the wing nut his side, and motioned that Cyril should do his. He did, the screen was pushed up, nuts tightened, a cooling breeze to please them both. They bowled merrily along, until Cyril realised that his pale blue suit was turning a rusty brown. Great amusement from Bill, until he realised his pale grey one was also changing colour. The radiator had boiled, rusty water on the bonnet had been blowing through the open window. Bill pulled into the side, waited till things cooled down, then picked up the bonnet to investigate. The top water hose had burst. They limped the car to a wayside garage, great good fortune they held a spare in stock. Hose fitted, suits mopped as clean as possible, hands washed under a cold tap, still a glorious day, so they pressed on. By the way, they did not know about Austin seven brakes.

I blanched at the thought. Harold nodded in understanding, took a few seconds to relight his pipe and carried on. Now Bill (unknown to Cyril) had decided that the best way to impress the ladies was to make an entrance in style. As soon as he reached the grass on the

Trent side at Gunthorpe, he swung the wheel hard right, and put the brake on. Not a lot happened, the car did begin to slow, slowly. They were still heading for the Trent. Cyril yelped (as he would) and grabbed the door chain to bale out, but it broke. The car did pull up, but not until the front wheels were well and truly in the water. Bill (always the unflappable) selected reverse. The Trent side is fairly steep and clay. The rear wheels spun a bit, and the car edged a little further in. Bill made a grab for his door chain, that broke. So he opened the window, reached out to the outside door handle to open the door. In came the Trent, so he shut it again, quickly, but he trapped his coat in the door. More water bubbled in to further 'condition' their suits.

"We canna stop 'ere," Cyril wailed, onlookers just 'looked on'. After what seemed an age, a large ponderous Policeman ambled over to them.

"Now then Sirs, what appears to be the trouble?".

We both must go, he to keep an appointment, me back to the call I had come to do. Still no one in. I crawled back in the car, smiling. It had been worth it all to see Harold again. A van pulled up in front of me. In neat painting on the back door it read. "Key and locksmith, your problems seen to, same day service." The rear doors were held together with string. Both Harold and Eric would appreciate that one.

Chapter 11
Sex Rears Its Ugly Head Yet Again

Friday again, already? "Tempus does fugit" I sighed as I turned into Station Road after crossing the little hump backed railway bridge. I thought of Eric. This was his exam weekend in London. I could picture his face, late last night, pinched with worry. I had pleaded that we give at a rest for a couple of nights, the rest would freshen him far more than working. He would have none of it. I had tried to tell him that what was not in his brain now, could not be crammed in panic. We had rowed about it, but the man was really desperate.

The last hour had been spent discussing 'it', rather than swotting 'it'.

My instructions. "Don't panic, read all the questions with care, two or three times, make sure you understand what they are asking, before you jump in and give the wrong answer. They may ask for any four out of five to be answered, if so, miss out the one your least sure of. Some will begin to write straight away, take no notice, take your time, DO NOT PANIC."

He had just kept nodding in a wan sort of way. I thought he was almost in a trance when we had parted. I pulled up in front of my first call, thought about him again for a few moments. If he keeps out of the pub, kept away from the others, got a good night's sleep, I had high hopes.

I was really tired, I struggled out of the car, wearily walked up the drive.

"You look as though you've not slept for a week," a

cheery voice called out from behind me. My customer, busy weeding the front border with a hand fork. A nice open scrubbed face, a happy smile, blonde hair, good figure, getting to be almost matronly, but a very very nice lady.

"I guess that is how I feel," I admitted, then briefly explained why I looked as I did.

"Well I have some good news to cheer you up," she smiled as she climbed to her feet. "Our Pat is getting married in the morning."

The impact of this unexpected news floored me. "She's not old enough."

"She's eighteen."

That also surprised me, she had always looked to me like a very pretty child, blonde hair, sparkling blue eyes, pert little figure, my guess would have been fifteen.

"She and her boy friend went to a party last week, they came in late Saturday night and dropped the bombshell, everything was already arranged. His Father is terminally ill, he wants to see a grandchild before he goes."

Doubt crossed my mind. "She is alright?"

"Oh yes, no shotguns."

"But the cost?"

"No problem, you know our Pat, she's always organised, a place for everything, and everything in its place. His side are paying for almost all. His Father has given them a cheque for ten thousand, Grandma another five thousand. There's an empty cottage on the farm."

Then I remembered, weeks ago, a Land Rover parked outside, a big ruddy faced man almost thirty, untidy sandy hair, his body spread, sprawled across the settee. I had assumed he was a family friend, wrong again, tomorrow he would be family.

Proud Mum walked with me up the drive towards the house. "All that made us give in, plus if the Father does die, Reg will inherit a seven hundred and fifty acre farm." I was busy thinking, I had never thought what a Reg should look like. He did look like a Reg really.

"What would they like for a wedding present?" The question was out before I had time to think about it.

"Pat again, organised through and through, she has a list, everything ticked off apart from a pair of double flannelette sheets."

I grinned, only this morning I had picked up such a pair, pristine in a cellophane wrapper, I turned and rushed back to the car. By the time I returned she was in the kitchen, two pass books and a ten pound note in her hand. She handed them to me.

Clear, if you please, apart from Pat not needing credit, they will be living too far out in the sticks for you to call."

I opened Pat's book first, she only owed two pounds, I filled in, signed with a flourish and handed eight pounds change. Mum shook her head a little sadly. "Mine as well. They are paying out a lot, but we have to try and do our share." Her book read eight pounds. With a sinking heart I cleared it. Two good customers lost, and it has cost me a pair of sheets to do it.

Within the hour I again I walked up Bert and Enid's path towards the front door. It burst open, and out rushed a glowing Mae. She armed me into the house, dropping the latch behind me. I did not notice. "Tea now or later?" she asked, bending over the tea things already on the table.

Unsuspecting, I said "now". She started to pour, both hands trembling, even the pots were dithering. I was drinking her in. A simple figure hugging dress, her pretty pert little bum facing me as she bent over the table.

"Mum and Dad have gone to a dance," she informed as she turned towards me with my tea, the cup and saucer were clattering like castanets. She handed me the tea and turned back to the table to get her own. At her waist three press studs gaped, through which I could see bare flesh.

"What have you got on under that dress?" I asked.

She turned towards me. "Not a stitch, and I was sixteen last Sunday." The tea cup in my hand was now rattling harder than ever.

"Y.Y. You're offering?"

"Offering, asking, pleading, use your own words, but I do intend to have you tonight. She stared at me, bold as brass, took my chattering pots, put them on the table, spilled almost all the tea in the process, came back towards me. "I've waited long enough, I want you now."

Before I had time to blink she had one arm round my neck, the other on my manhood, and was kissing me open mouthed. My struggle was quick to react, but not as quick as my erection. It felt as though it might burst my pants. I was pushed back into the settee, her tongue was in my mouth. I struggled, tried to protest, but almost lying back on the settee I was to say the least, disadvantaged. Almost in a daze, I now realised she was trying to undo my fly. Tempting, yes, I had been celibate

98

for some months, she was so young, well formed, desirable, but the young daughter of two best friends, it could not be. With an almost superhuman effort I managed to get hold of both her wrists, but she was as strong as a young tigress, we struggled chest to chest, the look in her eyes I am unable to describe, desperate, wanting, needing? We were both panting, I managed to gasp. "Please Mae, no." I put everything I knew into that plea.

"Why not?" she panted in return. "I want you, and I know you want me." Pressing her lower body towards me as though to feel she was right.

"Our age difference, your parents are two of my very best friends." I gabbled off all sorts of silly reasons in my panic.

"My friend's parents have a bigger age gap than you and I. I have no intentions of telling Mum and Dad. I will play safe, look." She broke away, rushed to her school satchel, came back brandishing a 'pack of three.'

I sat again, feeling as though my legs could not support me, dropped my head in my hands, moaned to anyone for help. I looked up to her in mute appeal. Her eyes now had a different message, they almost held a threat. "I have known about you all my life, I think I really loved you before I knew you. When we met, I realised that you were for me, ever since I have had a pain here." She touched herself. "Now you don't want me." She was close to tears.

I was tempted to take her in my arms to try and explain, but a warning bell rang within my mind. In a sort of 'big brother' way I did love the delectable creature, nothing could ever be more desirable, but! "What about your friends that have boasted about their conquests, Child like you are going to tell them" The wrong thing to say!!!!

"Child like, that's what you think, I am a child. Well look at this for a child's body." Her dress was off in a flash.

Yes, I was sexually experienced, yes I had had my moments, fumbling with clothes, usually in the dark, but I had never ever before seen a nude female. She was breathtaking, beautifully formed, a neat little triangle of curly pubic hair. Her hands caressed her breasts, her nipples hardened, grew, and almost glowed, my erection was throbbing, hurting. I put everything I knew into a plea. "Please Mae, I love you dearly, I am honoured, ashamed, please put your dress on before the temptation proves too much. You are beautiful, I would like to very much, but your parents, I would have to stop calling, they would want to know why."

I almost broke down as I picked her dress up and handed it to her. She put it on and ran from the room in tears. I stood for some time, trying to get my composure back. "No matter what I do I can't win," I told myself. "She will now hate me, if I follow her I just know I won't be strong enough to refuse again." I turned towards the door. Edna's pass book was on the sideboard, a ten shilling note poking out of the top. "Better take that or there will be questions." As I picked it up, an extra slip of paper fluttered to the floor. I picked it up. A note from Edna. "Ron, will you please call on my sister, tonight if at all possible. Her address is on the back. Edna. P.S. I do trust you."

I drew a deep breath, pocketed the money and the note, let myself out.

The bedroom window above opened, a tearful shaky voice threatened. "I shall tell them both you did."

"Who do you think they will believe?" In the hope it sounded more convincing than I felt.

Needless to say, my mind was in turmoil. What would she do? How would they react if she did? Who would they really believe? Over the years Bert and I had some real ding dongs with the boxing gloves. I was taller, more agile, but Bert was a strong powerful man. How could I make any attempt to defend myself if Bert thought the worst of me?

I must have done the rest of the calls in a daze, I finished almost two hours ahead of time, I had not chatted, not sold anything, my memory was a void. I pulled the car on to a grass verge, took out Edna's note, re read it again and again. "What does her sister want?" It sounds urgent. Why had she put I do trust you? I looked at my watch, I had never ever finished Friday night as early as this. I did have plenty of time to go and see her sister in Sibthorpe. I set off.

Slowed slightly for the little wriggle in the road at Gleadthorpe, a cycle leaning against the stone bridge over the river, a lady leaning beside it. As I neared, she walked towards the road side. Almost before she signalled me to stop, I realised that it was Linda. I pulled on to the grass and leaned over to open the door to ask what she was doing out here. Then realised that she was crying. I switched off and rushed round to her, put my arm around her shoulder's, enquired of the problem.

"I.I. need to talk to you," she managed to get out between sobs. Then tried to stem the flow with that daft little bit of lace.

"Take this," I instructed, handing her my always carried spare pristine man sized hanky. She wiped her eyes, then blew her nose in it.

"Did you mind me waiting for you? Are you early? Have you time to take me a little walk?"

I looked at my watch, then sort of thinking aloud. "Yes I am early, but I've had a request to go to Sibthorpe."

"I didn't know you went to Sibthorpe."

"I don't, this is a one off."

"It doesn't matter then," more tears.

"Oh I guess I can spare you half an hour."

"Are you sure?" then a coy look. "Bring your groundsheet."

I fished the groundsheet from under the seat, locked the car, and we went through the gate on to the Duke's estate.

In four hundred yards she nodded to a sloping mossy bank under an old oak. "That looks nice."

I spread the sheet, sat with my back to the tree trunk, lit up, and waited.

She did her sort of 'fold the legs and drop on them act'. I still waited.

Cigarette finished, I leaned over to stub it out on the tree root, then saw the most pretty miniscule flower. I nipped the head off to look at it more closely. Too small, I took my miniature 35 mm camera from my coat pocket, used the view finder in reverse to magnify. "Perfection in miniature," I muttered.

"What are you murmuring about?" she crawled over to me. I passed her the flower, camera, and instructed. Perfection in miniature," she agreed. "I would never have even seen it, or thought to use a camera that way. You are different." We took it in turns to marvel at it. Then, small as the flower was a teeny weeny little insect crawled from under a petal. Looking through the camera, it had tiny little pin prick eyes, legs certainly, as it moved, but no idea how many. I was engrossed, and started thinking aloud. "It must have a tiny little heart, kidneys, lungs, and either a little tassle or a little pussy, or there would never ever be any more of them."

WALLOP! she hit me, really hard. "And no one else but you would ever think of that either," she accused.

"Well it must or there would..." I stopped. Apart from being convulsed with laughter, she was giving me a most peculiar look.

"Are you going to extend your round to Sibthorpe?"

"I've not thought of it, I do need a bigger area, but this is a request to call on a customer's sister. Tonight if at all possible. So let's be hearing your problem and I can be off."

"It's my husband," she burst into tears again.

I put one arm round her shoulders, nestled her head on mine, and waited, then eventually instructed. "Get it off your chest lass, I've not got all night.".

Hesitatingly, she explained. "My husband has been smacking me," pause, "Again."

"I've heard some ladies like that."

"No, hard, it really hurts, he says that if he smacks it does not leave a bruise, so that I can't report him." She raised her head to look at me with red rimmed eyes. "I could stay here for ever."

"No you can't. I've got work to do." I looked down, that same old blouse again, another button had popped, no bra. He breast 'nestled' no other word for it. The pinky brown nipple was in view, I could reach it if I stretched my fingers. Tempted, I resisted, then pleaded with her to tell it all, my crutch was hardening, again.

"You know I have two children?" I tried to nod. "I think that is enough." She wriggled, giving me an even better view, I never even thought to nod. "He's always wanting me to, y'know, and he won't take precautions, when I ask him to he smacks me. He's only on the roads at the pit, poor money, when they put him on the face, and good money, he gets a bad back and stops going to work. Secretly, I think he's frightened of the face.

But he does go round digging gardens for pensioners, for free. No income, so what I've saved soon goes. My Sister and my Mum try to help out, but it's not fair on them. I get him three hundred cigarettes a week on the Co-op order, with no income, I can't, so he smacks me again."

I was about to suggest he should buy his own fags, but she was in full flow again.

"He tips all his wages up to me every week, then tells everybody, so they all think how good he is. But then it's my responsibility to pay all the bills. I can't when he's not at work, so he smacks me again." She looked up at me, eyes filling with tears again.

Without thinking, I bent and kissed her in the centre of her forehead, she nuzzled up to me like a baby. Then she was slipping, I almost chuckled as I thought 'silk knickers'. But when she put a hand on my growth to push herself erect, all such thoughts went. Had she noticed?

"How's your foot?" wriggle wriggle. "Your feet don't smell."

"I thought I told you, if your feet smell and your nose runs you are upside down." I doubt if she had even heard me. She looked up at me, her eyes were almost doe like. Another button had popped, a super pair, very tempting. All now in view, big nipples. My 'hardness' was getting harder by the second. I stretched my fingers, straightened my wrist, and ever so gently tweaked that hardening peak. She looked up at me, the look sort of said, "Who's a naughty boy then?" Put her hand on my bulge, pushed herself up to kiss me full on the mouth. Her mouth tasted so clean, so fresh. It was all so pleasant, also painful, and I realised that I was now even bigger than during the Mae episode. I sort of sighed, turned her, so that I could get my other hand on her other breast. I was now tweaking both nipples at once, and, they were growing. My move had almost unbalanced her. She moved her right leg over both mine, so that she was kneeling astride my legs. Our tongues were probing each other's mouth, the breathing was heavy, again I realised how fresh and clean her mouth tasted. By now, I was kneading her full breasts, whilst still working on those nipples, then I realised, she was undoing my fly. It gave no resistance, was open in a flash. Her hand was inside my jockey shorts, she was holding it, and trying to pull it out with brute force.

No way would it bend, I tried to arch my back, to help, allow more room, but sitting as I was I could not move enough. She just kept pulling with all her might. With a rending of cotton, my pants split, releasing him.

She gasped "oops sorry, that's nice," then kissed it on its really throbbing end.

I was struggling to keep control of my emotions, all this so soon after the Mae episode was proving too much. Then, she took as much as possible in her mouth and twirled her tongue round the end. My back arched, my whole body went into spasm, I jerked, convulsed, my head going back and forward beyond my control, then I climaxed. "If I have to die let it be now," seemed to be my thoughts as I slowly came back to normal. I mumbled "Very sorry, I have never experienced anything like that before, that really was too much."

"Neither have I, I read about it ages ago, I've been thinking about it ever since, it's nice, I liked it."

"I had better go and get myself cleaned up."

"No need," dabbing her mouth with that silly little hanky.

"How does one follow that?" I was thinking as I struggled to get up. I levered myself on to one elbow, it slipped, my head banged on the tree trunk with a hollow thud. Her gasp of concern was cut off when I looked behind her and said "How do you do." She jerked around, trying to catch the flaps of her open blouse to cover her chest, a look of absolute horror on her face. No one there. Then she spotted the fiendish grin on my face, she lashed out at me, till seeing the funny side, she collapsed across me, crying, but with laughter this time.

We must have lain almost ten minutes like that, till I realised that I needed to pee. I wriggled in discomfort. "Something wrong?"

"I need to ease myself."

"Sorry." She lifted her body off mine, still kneeling, and began to fasten her blouse, I went behind a tree a few yards away. When I came back, she was still kneeling with that half amused smile on her face. I bent and kissed the centre of her forehead. Her hands were feeling for me again. I was about to tell her that I was not that good, when I realised that he was in fact showing signs of life. Her cool nimble hands really did have a magic touch. Whilst she was rejuvenating, I again undid her blouse buttons, and rolled her on her back.

I rolled and tweaked one breast with my left hand, whilst my right explored up her thigh. Very soft, silky smooth skin. French knickers, silk, with very wide legs. Her triangle was soaking wet. I wet it some more with a few deft finger movements on her clitoris, then used two fingers inside whilst the thumb did more for the magic little lump. By now, with no pants offering resistance, flies open fully, she pulled him towards her promised land. A wink is as good as a nod anytime. I obliged. Then, so gently, I entered, but only just, then withdrew again. I was watching her face, surprise, horror? Then I went all the way in one solid thrust. She gasped and began to stir beneath me. I used a long slow rhythm, all the way, each and every time. Each and every thrust produced a gasp, her head began to thrash from side to side. Then I knew fear, her eyes suddenly rolled upwards, I could only see the whites, she looked for all the world as though she had gone. In fear I stopped movement, her eyes returned to normal, looking so hurt. Again, with almost superhuman control I kept the thrusts long and slow. She began to whimper, then shout. "Oh no, yes, yes, yes."

I had to give way, and pumped at full speed.

"Ohhhh," she yelled as we both climaxed. Just in time, I withdrew, clutching him firmly before the dangerous spurt. We both lay a while till the gasping and panting had subsided, then I rolled away, got up, and sort of shambled behind my tree again.

Back I came, she was again 'Miss Prim', all buttoned up, with an expression like the cat that got all the cream. "Today has been my most marvellous day ever, thank you." She used my waist to pull herself erect, had a quick little fondle. Then picked up the groundsheet, folded it neatly, put it over one arm, the other through mine, we walked in a dreamy sort of way back to the car. I put the groundsheet back, she clung to me for a moment, then cycled off. The bike wobbling well over half the road width as she did.

I watched her go, until I struggled to sit on the bridge parapet, lit a cigarette, and thought deeply. I don't think I will ever forget today either. Have I really ruined everything? There's no doubt, a standing tool has no conscience at all.

Looking at my watch, almost nine o'clock, do I go or not? Go lad, if a light is on, call, if not, don't. I pulled up outside the address given. One light on upstairs, one light on downstairs. Nothing is ever easy. I switched the engine off to think. The front door opened, a slimmer, taller, older version of Edna walked towards me. She crossed to the other side of the car and motioned that she wanted the door opening, I did so, she got in, wriggled herself comfortable, looked at me with a face full of disproval, then spoke. "I can only assume that you are not the gentleman that Edna thinks you are?"

I looked at her in astonishment. "Sorry I am so late," I blurted.

"It's not that, we both knew and realised that Mae has a crush on you, but Edna knew that you could be trusted. Now you turn up looking as though you have spent a good hour on the nest, so I assume Edna is wrong to have such faith in you?"

I sighed with relief. "Edna could trust me, but the lady I have just left should not have done."

She laughed out loud. "Edna said that you were straight to the point of rudeness, I like it, I'm Clare, the big sister, pleased to meet you." She offered her hand. Her grip was firm, warm, and dry. "Come on in." she instructed.

"But the light upstairs," I questioned.

"Oh, that's hubby, he's been in bed an hour, he's reading, he will still be reading long after I am abed and asleep. Before we were married he pestered me all he time, now that we are married he has no interest."

She led the way back up her garden path and through the front door, parked me in the front room, promised tea before I could blink, and turned towards the kitchen.

Hesitatingly, I asked, "Do you think I may use your toilet?"

"Sure, nooky always makes you pee," another laugh.

109

She led the way back into the hall. "Toilet that away, kitchen this away, I will see you where I dumped you back away." As she spoke her fingers pointed out the various doors, I was smiling at her unusual instructions till I spotted the note on the loo door. "The wee room." I almost had to laugh out loud.

Talk about relief, I had a very tender member, it was really hurting now, the discomfort decided me. I dropped my trousers, removed the torn underpants, had a gentle pee, replaced trousers, and tucked the torn pants in my jacket pocket, muttered "Street bin," to myself, then feeling a trifle more comfortable I returned to the room. Tea already poured, a Piccadilly cigarette and lighter waiting beside my cup. "Nice, I used to almost smoke these."

"Start on them again, you will smoke far less than you do your cheaper ones," she advised. "Right then, explanations are due from me." I almost managed to start and protest. "Our Edna is right, your the sort that can be trusted, I admit that we were both worried, young Mae really does want you, and with her sort of ground bait it will take a very strong man to refuse. By the way, Bert has no idea." A huge sigh of relief escaped me. "I will not ask what happened, but if you say that you did not fall by the wayside, that's good enough for me."

I think I was really glowing at that recommendation. "You wouldn't let a lady down anyway, so let's drop the subject."

We talked the tea pot dry, Edna, Mae, Bert, the difference the war had made to us all, Morals, money, attitudes. The way the modern youth thought nothing of doing what we had all been scared to do. I took a casual glance at my watch. Eleven thirty. I shot to my feet, "I must be off, look at the time."

"Sit yourself down, I have not finished with you yet." My worry beads began to chatter. "Do you sell sets of kitchen furniture, y'know, the table and four chairs?"

"Yes."

"Well, bring or send me a set."

"What colour?"

"I leave it with you."

"Price?"

"I leave that with you," smiling at my discomfort, she asked me to 'come through', we went to the 'thisawy' room. Nice, sensible, two doors in opposite corners, window on the right of the fireplace straight ahead. It looked to be about twelve or thirteen feet square, almost anything would 'go'. But all the help I got was. "I leave it with you."

Even as she eased me out through the front door, shook my hand, kissed me on the cheek, she whispered. "I leave it with you."

I drove off towards home, slow, thoughtful, what a day. Mae would now hate me, Linda was an unknown worry now, I was not giving all my thoughts to driving, I should have been. I blinked my tired eyes and peered ahead, had I seen it? Or was it imagination? There it was again, a firefly in the middle of the road. "It can't be," I muttered to myself. "This is England, not India." Automatically my right foot shifted to 'cover' the brake. I put the lights on to 'main beam'.

"Silly bugger," I expostulated as a drunk hove into

111

view, complete with glowing cigarette end. He staggered to the road side, waving me through with his hand held cigarette, he stared bemused at me as I drove slowly past, going right to the other side of the road to do so. I glanced across at him. Mr Swift. I realised as I built up speed and felt in my pocket for cigarettes and lighter. Not there? I felt in my other pocket, yes, but a piece of rag as well. "What th'" My underpants of course. I dropped them on the passenger's seat and wondered 'where to'. Entered the colliery village, now almost totally in darkness. Then I grinned, cut the engine, and allowed the car to coast to a standstill just before the Swift household. Pants in hand, a silent run round the back, pants in the Swift dustbin, back to the car, take off on tick over, till I was well out of earshot, then accelerate into the night.

Just over two miles, a glow of light on the left, funny, not seen that before. I thought, then remembered a lot of building activity, local rumour was a small factory to make spanners. I got nearer, a floodlit sign stated 'Robert's Tool works.' I smiled and thought aloud. "So does mine, but I don't need a floodlit sign to advertise the fact."

Unusual for me, I was up early in the morning, needed to pee as well, I shot up the yard as quick as possible. 'It', was small, black, limp, sore, should I take it to the Doctor? No, he would ask awkward questions.

Chapter 12
A Favour For A Friend

Well before nine the phone rang. It was Eric's wife. Would I do Eric a big favour?

"Of course, for Eric, but he's in London."

Irritated she said "Of course, she knew. But did I know her Mother. Eric's Mother in Law?"

Yes I had heard a lot, but nothing I was prepared to admit, she sounded as nutty as a fruit cake to me. So I muttered something about "never having had the pleasure," and waited.

"My Mum does not, and never has, liked Eric, she thinks he is a boozer, a womaniser, in fact all she thought was bad. I dare not tell her that he is in London without me, he will be accused of having a lads weekend, pubs and brothel creeping. He phoned me before he went into the exam this morning, the car coil has gone again, he can't do a thing about it till Monday morning, so it has to be well after lunch before he can get back home.   T h e problem is, a well to do relation in Yorkshire has left a parcel of clothing at an Electrical shop in Ashborne. They are stocktaking tomorrow, Sunday, and she has said that Eric will call then to collect the parcel. If it's not here by Monday morning she will smell a rat. It would clear so many possible problems if you could collect for Eric."

"For Eric, yes of course, how did he seem?

She was rushing, but managed to say that she thought he seemed more worried about the car than the exam. Good! With a pleased grin I put the receiver down...

Sunday dawned, a terrible day, two top coats colder, dark clouds, rain. I had thought of giving the car a wash first. Silly, get an early start.

I threw a heavy coat in the back (in case) and was on my way before nine. Yawning, and thinking the jobs you get saddled with for a friend. In view of the weather I decided to keep to the lower route via Blepper. Even so, as I got further into the hills, the worse the weather became. As I skirted the road end down to the Ford and Tilminton, I gasped with surprise. Globules of ice were forming on the windscreen. I pulled into the side and scrabbled through my tool bag. With a sigh of relief I found the two rubber window wedges that I 'hoped' were there. I picked up the bonnet, one side, then the other, and put a wedge under the back of it. This would allow 'some' warm air to deflect up the windscreen. With great care I set off again, the steering was very light, pebbles were hitting the underside of the mudguards, sure signs it was freezing hard.

The traffic lights in the centre of Asbon were stuck on red, whilst waiting I could look around. Almost straight opposite was the shop I wanted. Fed up with waiting, I crept over the still red traffic lights, turned right, then curved left up to the market square. As I hoped, only six cars including my own. I parked right in the middle. Put on my coat (glad I brought that) and retraced back to the lights and shop. The shop lights were on, but repeated knocks on two separate doors produced no response what ever. Above the shop window was the phone number, across the road was a phone box. Fishing in my pocket for change I scuttled across. The phone rang and rang, no reply.

The shop door opened, a young lad stepped out, I ran across, too late, he had slammed the door behind him. Muttered discussion proved he did work there, they were stock taking, he was going to the pub for sandwiches, but the manager had threatened sudden death if anyone was let in.

"Is this Fort bloody Knox where all the bullion is stored?" I snarled at the lad. No doubt he was scared of me, but even more so of the manager. He had been given a secret knock to regain access. No way would he divulge it. The poor kid was between the devil and the deep. He went to the pub, whilst I hunched up in the doorway in an effort to get out of the biting wind.

It seemed ages before he returned, gave his knock, I was in before him. Looking straight into the eyes of a familiar face. The eyes looking back were just as astonished. It seemed ages before anyone spoke, then light dawned. "Mauripur," I said.

He nodded.

"Seventy Seven Squadron, Wireless."

"Seventy Seven Radar, next office." We grinned and shook hands. Asked each other how we were, when did we get home etc. then the displeased Manager arrived. When introduced light dawned,

"You're the chap for the parcel?"

All pals now, they shared their tea and sandwiches with me, almost but not all were ex R.A.F. either wireless or Radar bods, we had all been trained at the same camps, if at different times. The manager had to break it up. "We are now behind with the stocktaking, but in any

115

case, a weather warning on the wireless advises everyone to keep off the roads, a band of freezing drizzle and fog has caused dozens of accidents already.

I puzzled all by asking had anyone got a potato? The young lad was sent into the yard they shared with a greengrocer to look, whilst I explained that a fresh cut potato rubbed on the windscreen helped to stop ice forming. Yes, he found two, wizened, but possibles. Handshakes all round, time to go, off I went. Head down I walked back to where I had left the car, looked up, no car! All of them had gently slid down to the bottom of the slope. I picked up one leg to go down to them, the other shot from under me, my backside hit the tarmac with a solid thump. A voice behind began to ask "Are you all," Another thump. I turned to see an older man, also on his bottom.

"It's worse than any ******* ice rink," he complained.

All obvious now, the drizzle had frozen as it landed, the slope had done the rest, we both walked back to the shop as if on eggs.

In no time at all bodies were pushing cars sideways, anyways, two more thoughtfuls had put extra socks on over their shoes. The biggest problem, some cars having been pushed clear, just drifted back down to the bottom of the slope again.

All were Abson residents, none could ever remember a situation as bad as this. I was offered accommodation for the night rather than risk the journey. But my parents, Eric's Mother in Law, Eric's wife, I just dare not accept.

I gently coaxed the wheels into motion, but steering

116

had no effect, it angled its way across the road until the wheels hit the kerb and pointed me down hill. She sailed on till the reached the right hand bend, hit the curb and put me in the right direction. I managed a wry smile as I wondered what I would have done had a needed to go the 'other' way. The main road south had a slight camber to the left, she slid left. No matter what I tried she slid towards the drop. Eventually, second gear, on tick over only seemed to hold it. As I passed a low hedge I had a quick glance, a ten foot drop into a grass field, a car on its side. At the next lights (not working) I turned left for Blepper. More camber, the slight bend had me looking down a twenty foot banking, a lorry upside down at the bottom. Four hundred yards further, a lorry was in the hedge bottom, it had snapped a telegraph pole off on route, but the pole was still suspended by the wires. A few slow careful miles later, a group of five cars, discarded, all willy nilly all over the place, I shuffled my way through them. The cold was intense, the accelerator was between the brake and the clutch, it came through a hole in the floorboards, so did the cold draught, straight up my trouser leg. I had somehow managed to tuck my trouser bottoms in my socks without stopping. My right leg had been numb for over an hour, I was bursting for a pee, I just had to keep going, as once I lost momentum, would I ever get going again? Different road surfaces, angles, cambers, all needed careful different treatment. After hours of the most difficult motoring I had ever experienced, the frost began to give. Over the last few miles I actually saw thirty miles per hour on the speedo. I pulled up outside Eric's home, and thanked those rough, hard swearing, knowledgeable mechanics, that had drilled into me all I now knew.

Chapter 13
It All Begins To Fall Apart

A bad night, tired out, tense after yesterday, I did not really wake up, but got up, still asleep I suppose. I went up the yard and used it, had another look at it. Still a rubbery little black painful appendage, but in parts it was turning yellow. Almost awake, I realised, being up this early, I had time to call at the shop for Clare.

I walked in at one minute past nine, everyone was aghast, the Manager, first to recover. "My word, we are bright and early this morning."

Just managing to stifle a yawn, I gave a sheepish grin, and admitted that I had in fact had a few rough days and nights.

"You want to think you are lucky that you live where you do. On the radio this morning they were saying what terrible conditions Staffordshire, Derbyshire and Cheshire had yesterday. It appears it rained and froze, hundreds of accidents, cars sliding all over the place, it was chaos, we are lucky."

I replied. "Yes we are," and made my way to kitchen furniture. Two sets only, a bright red, and a sickly green, neither remotely Clare. "Any catalogues?" I asked the chap in charge.

"No, you will have to see the manager, he keeps them all."

"Another bloody silly idea," I growled as I retraced my steps towards the office door.

H.H.Have you got your l.l.ledgers with you by any chance?"

"Yes, they are in the car, why?"

M.M. My secretary needs to see them."

Without another word, I spun on my heels and went out, picked up the ledgers and thumped them in front of her. Then asked the manager for kitchen furniture catalogues.

W.W. What do you w.w.want them for?"

"What do you think? I have a customer interested."

"G.G.Give me her name and address, I will post her one."

"No good mate, she has left the choice to me."

He could not take this in, he stuttered, stammered on about never ever hearing anything like it. How could I expect him to place an order on my say so, what could he do if she rejected it?

My temper was bubbling, my steam pressure was rising. Then, Fussy Breeches appeared at the door and whispered in his ear.

"J.J.Just a minute," and he backed through the door, closed it behind him.

I looked at the closed door and wondered, I was ragged, and knew it. Shall I barge in or bugger off home? My 'tackle' was hurting, I was worried about the look on 'her' face. Feeling in my pocket for cigarettes and lighter, no time, he was back.

"About Mrs. Priest," he started, not a trace of stutter, he was on firm ground.

"Titchfield Street Mrs, Priest?"

"You have no others by that name."

"She is either never in, or won't answer the door."

"So you have said many times, neither she or Mrs.

Swift have ever paid you anything."

"Well you call and collect the buggers, don't tell me, show me."

"Mrs. Swift is a canvasser's call, Mrs. Priest is one of your own productions, you insisted she had a high credit rating."

"It's one of Dad's workmates, if Dad says he's straight, he is. Remind me of the balance.

"I would have thought that you should know only too well, nothing since the original two shillings, balance six pounds eight shillings. I will give you two weeks, if nothing in that time we will take it all from your wages."

"Eric's face and words came into view, he had warned me of this. I took out my wallet, extracted the only six pounds in it, fiddled in my trouser pocket for change, and handed it over. "Get her to give me a receipt for this and close the account."

"Y.Y. you can't do that."

"I just have." Stalking out of the shop, I leaned on the wall beside the window, and lit up. Dad's words came back to me. "Do you want a new customer?"

"Yes, if they pay."

"There's not a straighter man down t' pit, he works every hour God sends. He's only on t' roads, but with all the time he puts in he must be getting twice as much as me. Name Bill Priest, address, 14 Titchfield Street."

Then the conversation with his wife, who had not impressed. "I can't afford much today Mr. Chapman, just take two shillings now, then I can give you a pound when you call on Saturday."

Because of Dad, I had agreed, never seen her since, I

had called on all days, at all times of day. I had dared to mention it to Dad just the once. His lips had tightened. "I told you, there's not a straighter man down that bloody pit."

I looked at my watch, the early shift on, would be coming up about now. It was worth a try. I trod on my cigarette and set off. Not a thought about the shop half day.

In twenty minutes I was parked round the corner, just off the main road, within seconds a pit bus pulled up. Almost a full bus load rushed off and tore towards their homes, I momentarily wondered if they were all on a promise. Then three older men got off, grunted their way towards home. Last off, a very tall man, bowed with fatigue, he lowered himself slowly from the platform, with a laboured tread he set off towards me. I rushed back to the car and parked it round the corner, got out, waited.

He got level. "Bill Priest?" I questioned.

"That's me."

"I'm Jack's lad, Ron Chapman, sorry, but that stuff I let your wife have, she's only paid me two bob.

A huge sigh escaped the man. "Sorry, take your car to the top of the street, walk back, I will meet you in the Greenhouse of number sixteen." Another sigh. "Promise, I will be with you in under ten minutes."

Doubt, but he looked so distressed, I weakened and nodded. I followed his instructions, went into the greenhouse, waited, within eight minutes, he joined me, bent to the fireplace, opened the door, took out two tobacco tins, replaced one, opened the other, initials W.P.

painted on it. "How much?"

"Six Pounds Eight."

He counted it out and handed it over. "Sorry, she really is a bugger, I can't keep pace with her debts. If ever you do trust me again, please deal with me, not her." It was all so serious, we shook hands and parted.

I let the car coast down the hill. A lady from the Greenhouse house walked across the road, signalled me to stop, I did, "Please come into my house." Puzzled, I complied. She had said please, but it was more like a command than a request.

I followed her up her path, a little scotch blood by the way she rolled her R's in a most provocative way. A good figure, slightly over weight, very good legs, tight bra straps showing beneath her blouse. I followed into her kitchen. Everything glowed with cleanliness, as she turned towards me, I realised she was also squeaky clean."

"Ron Chapman?" Statement or question? I nodded.

"I'm Dot England," nice smiling open face. " I think I should explain about poor Bill, he has to hide his 'spare' in our Greenhouse, otherwise she spends it. To save his embarrassment, we also keep a tin of 'spare' in there. It's handy sometimes. She roared with laughter.

I tried to join in with her amusement, but my noise was hollow in comparison. My 'bits' hurt, the look on the face of 'fussy breeches', I was worried.

"You don't look well lad, fancy a cup o' tea?"

"That sounds like a good idea to me," I tried to force a smile as I said it. She put out her hand to shake mine, a warm friendly 'I'm really pleased to know you shake'.

She turned and went to the sink, in no time at all the pots were laid, kettle singing.

"That's quick."

"I know, one of your firm's quick boiling kettles, it wasn't cold anyway, my man has just gone to work. I bought it from your bloke pushing trade, but he wanted credit, I said no credit, cash or no sale, I won."

Tea poured, Park Drive and lighter produced. "Now what's your problem? I have a very sympathetic ear." She sipped her tea and went on. "Work? women? Pain in your marriage tackle? You need help my laddee?"

I could only gasp.

"It's up to you. Ten years married, sixteen years nursing on a men's ward, I still help out with marital pains from the pit. Far better me, here, than all the leg pulls if they go to the ambulance room."

"How how?"

"Tell you, seen it all, a lot of it down the pit you know, men do just not know how to look after their bits. They burn them, drop things on them, get them fast in various sorts of daft places. Then when they go to sleep they keep their hands on it to protect it." With a hearty laugh, she threw her hands up in mock horror. "I think that's why the Lord invented men. To sow the seed, and give women something else to look after. Now are you going to confide in me?"

I don't know what I mumbled, all this was beyond me. Just met the woman and she was talking to me as though we had 'schooled' together. Too intimate all together for me.

"What are you doing for the rest of the day, still

working, or is it your half day?"

Half day rang a bell, I looked at my watch, twenty to one. I shot to my feet. "Sorry, must go, had not realised, can I call again?"

She nodded, smiled and waved a good bye, as I shot from her home.

Just after one o' clock when I got to the shop, all but the manager had gone, lights going off as he killed switches.

Churchill met me with a curt, "Where did you shoot off to? in my office if you please." Turning, he led the way into his emporium.

"I have only nipped back for my ledgers," I started.

"You can't have them, my P.A. has been through them, you have paid in thirty four pounds fifteen shillings short since we last checked your books."

I could not help it, shock I suppose. "YOU HAVE GOT TO BE BLOODY WELL JOKING."

"No, I'm not, and do not shout or use that tone to me."

I glowered at him, now realising the firm determination on his face. "You are really serious?"

"Yes, very, and I'm waiting."

"For what?" I ground out through gritted teeth.

"Your explanation."

"Is this her idea or yours?"

"Miss Alcock found, I checked, she's right."

My mind raced, it was not possible, for the last two weeks I had had to put a few bob in to balance, I admitted this to him.

"So you admit, you do make mistakes?"

"Don't you, ever?"

"Of course not, I'm the manager."

"It must be very nice to be as perfect, have you caught it off her?"

Then I realised the truth of the situation.

"Are, you, doubting, my honesty?" Came slowly, through clenched teeth as the temper began to bubble.

"Oh n.no, M.Mr, Ch.Ch. Chapman, n.n.not at all, b.b. but you must have m.made m.mistakes. I have to make the b.b.books b.balance."

"Get the bloody ledgers, we will go through them now."

"N.Not p.p.possible, I p.promised my wife I would today take a proper half day."

"What about my collections?"

That nonplussed him. "W.W. we did not find the seriousness till after John Kirk had gone, or I would have asked him. He will be with you to check your pass books in the morning."

"Missing today's collection will kill off any hopes of commission this week."

"That's your problem I'm afraid."

I turned away before I hit him, then turned back. "Tell Mr John Bloody Kirk to bring his bike. I'm not riding him round to drop me in it."

Next morning, after a virtually sleepless night, the phone rang early. I staggered down to answer it.

"Morning Ron, Super John here, can we meet early? I've a lot to tell and ask you. PLEASE listen to me before you blow your top. Oh, and please bring your car, your extended round will be a bit much for me these days on a bike."

I agreed, and arranged to meet him off the bus. He was a 'firm's' man, but straight, I did trust him. I washed, shaved, toyed with breakfast, cleaned my teeth, and set off to meet him. Mum knew 'summat's were up' but she kept a discreet silence

Worry, fear, puzzles were in my mind as I waited. I began to realise that temper would not help, not fair to John. "Keep in control," I promised myself.

I realised, he looked pensive, as he rolled himself up to get in my little car. I took him to a drive off Dubdy common, neither had said a word. I switched off and turned to him. He offered a Player's cigarette. "I didn't know you smoked." I started.

"Used to, gave up, but this lot has got me on edge," he lit, drew a huge lungful and almost choked. When recovered, he almost pleaded. "Hear me out before you even consider blowing your top. I am supposed to check all travellers' pass books at least every ten weeks. What with one thing and another, yours have almost gone fifteen. Chap's ill, etc. I kept saying that yours could be lcft."

"So you're in it as well?"

He almost looked bashful as he nodded. "For what it's worth, I'm as puzzled as you. Apart from Miss Alcock's attitude."

"You don't like her do you?"

"I can't stand the smelly bitch."

"So it won't come as a surprise to realise she does not like you?"

"No."

127

"You will not be able to use what I am going to say, I would deny it anyway, but I think you should know, and know what I think. I have a feeling she is trying to fix you, and if we're not careful, she will." I looked puzzled, opened my mouth, then shut it like a goldfish as his hand went up. "Hell hath no fury like." Then looked at me with a most peculiar expression.

If it had not all been so serious, I think I would have burst out laughing.

"Have you not realised that she fancies you?"

"Don't be daft, she's engaged anyway." I was horrified at the thought.

"Well, put it another way, you have a bit of a reputation with the ladies, she may have wanted to find out if it was true. Do you remember the firm's staff outing to the coast last year?"

"Of course."

"The ones with cars, were asked to ferry the non car owners home."

"Yes."

"You were adamant, your car could only carry four, yet I have seen you bring four customers in to the shop, with you driving, that's five, why?"

"The fourth and last drop would have been her, that stink in my little car for almost an hour, no thanks."

"Who was your last drop?"

"Miss Cookson, why?"

"What happened?"

Silence.

"You did hear me Ron?" I nodded. "Well let me guess, you, at least, had a strong snogging session with

Miss Cookson, she told Miss Alcock, and she did not like what she heard."

"Women don't," I started.

"Oh yes they do, they are worse than men at telling of their conquests."

I blanched at the memory, had she told all? Coat, blouse and bra off, my pants around my ankles, Miss Cookson had been a real ball of fire. I shuddered and worried.

"That was your first mistake, you made the second yesterday."

"What, how?" My mind was in turmoil.

"By paying that bad debt yourself, if you can afford to do that, you may well be on the fiddle."

That did it, "NO WAY" I shouted, "I was down to copper's after paying it, but I got it all back from her husband yesterday."

John's hand went up to silence me. "You promised," he reminded. Then added. "I'm glad about that. My sister is nice, a homely sort of girl, so I think that Bernard is a bit overboard having a bit of flash like Miss Alcock at the shop. In his eyes, as yet, she can do no wrong."

I was really lost, and said so.

"Bernard is my brother in law." The news, and realisation seeped through. He went all business like again. "Let's get these pass books checked, as soon as they realise that this end is alright we can sort the office side out.

First call, we were met by.

"Hello Raff, I heard you had been sacked for dishonesty, but no reports of a murder, so it can't be right." Nearly all had heard 'something', I was glowering in no time.

John was great, he cajoled, coaxed, and said that he too was puzzled as to how the news had got around, and so quickly. "Try not to get upset." He pleaded.

"You're too bloody late, I already am." We came out of the last call, I turned and said, "I suppose I can see her bloody ledgers, to check against my own?"

"It's against the rules, but this is so serious, you have every right, we will do it next Thursday morning when these pass books have been checked.

The firm's method for travellers paying in, was. A large sheet of paper, with all the folio numbers in order, a space at the side of each number for that week's payment. Each column of figures were totalled, the totals transposed to an extra column at the end, these in turn were totalled, the answer being the amount the traveller should hand in. Quite simple?

The following week, office girls extracted the figures, entered them into the office ledgers. Then the balances should all agree. Customers' pass books, collecting ledgers, and shop ledger.

We were all gathered in the office, early, next Thursday morning. Her ledger was open on her desk, John stood with my collecting ledgers under his arm. Churchill was looking at me with great trepidation.

I upset the apple cart in no time. "Can we have a window open to get rid of this awful smell." She bristled, Churchill stuttered and said nowt, John motioned me to cool it.

"Now for my paying in sheets."

"You don't want them," from a startled Fussy Breeches.

"Of course I do, Super has checked my ledgers with their pass books, Mr Churchill has checked your ledger, now we need to agree my sheets with your entries." She clucked, Churchill almost spoke, John was struggling to keep a straight face, she got on her knees and produced the paying in sheets from under her desk.

"N. N. Now," started the manager.

"Shurrup an' mek yoursen useful," I instructed. "This is my job, my reputation and my money on the line here."

To anyone listening, I asked. "Any sheet any date, any payment, read it please." The first five were spot on. Then I asked, "Why the different coloured ticks?"

John explained, each colour denotes a four week period, then in case of a query, we know which colour to check.

"Colours always used in the same rotation?"

"Yes, of course."

"Could someone tell me who Folio 256 is? I'm sure it's Mrs Stranger, 15 Elm Street, if I'm right, there is a mistake here."

"Of course not," she protested.

"No one, not even you, is mistake proof." I pointed out.

Super John said yes it was Mrs. Stranger.

"She's the best customer I've got, it's a fight to keep her in debt, she has never ever paid less than a pound, two some weeks, and on occasions five. But you have down here a lot of five shilling payments. Explain that," I smirked, handing her the sheet.

Looking over her shoulder, I spotted another I thought familiar. "I also think that 343 is Mrs Measured, she pays ten shillings every week, never varies, and never misses, down here you've got quite a few misses, and some five bob payments."

John checked, I was right again. I picked up a paying in sheet in case another 'familiar' caught my eye. Some of the paper looked different, I moved behind her and held it up to the light, it was thinner in part's, I sniffed at it, no doubt. All oozing charm, oily smooth, so full of innocence, I asked. "Is there by any chance a bottle of Milton in the office?"

"Why yes," she says, "in my drawer, have you hurt yourself?"

"No, but I think you have. Who told you that you could erase ink with Milton?"

"My brother."

"Ex R.A.F.?"

"Yes, how do you know?"

"We have all altered far too many weekend passes to not know." She fled from the office, her blush was almost the colour of her hair.

"Who has the biggest round?"

"Mr. Mack, but his is a town round, not a scattered country one like yours."

"How many customers?

"Just under six hundred."

"Now who has the smallest?"

"Don Phillips."

"How many?"

"Almost three hundred."

"Well, how come Don has payments against numbers almost up to six hundred? Look at all these pound payments under 343." Consternation all round, as all tried to look at once.

SHE, came back, almost on cue, she'd had a further bash with the perfume bottle. "Miss Wyatt,"

"Miss Wyatt what?" I questioned.

"I.I. It was a young girl we set on to do the books, it was too much for her, I had to ask her to leave."

I just could not believe it.

"I had to alter a lot of her work after she had gone," from a still blustering, blushing Miss Alcock.

"You put a young girl with no experience on a job as important as this?"

I just could not believe my ears.

"You see I had to alter a lot of her work after she had gone."

"Milton?" I enquired with a smirk.

Her head bowed, almost in shame, only almost.

It was late lunch by the time we had sorted as much as possible. Fussy Breeches admitted there were mistakes, but no intent. Churchill said he would pay office overtime if need be to get it all checked? Super John had rushed off to catch his bus. I walked out, head held high, my ledgers tucked beneath my arm. Rung out, yes, but I would soon feel fine.

Mr. Churchill rushed out after me. "I.I. don't know if I.I. should ask, b.b.but I'm desperate. C.C.Could I ask a great favour of you?"

I hesitated, thought, if I said no it would smell of

sour grapes, it seemed that he had been fair with me. Awe, what the hell. "Yes if I can, what is it?"

"We have a customer in Bull Farm, I promised her that I would deliver her a spring interior mattress, all this worry had put it out of my mind. It's too late to get a carrier now, could we put it on your car roof?"

I thought long and hard, a fabric roof, I had only recovered it with an ex Army gas cape a few weeks ago. at least five coats of tyre black on it.

But Churchill was not practical enough to understand, so I did not tell him. I could use the faithful groundsheet from under the seat to put the mattress on. "Alright." I agreed.

We struggled up the stairs from the basement carrying the mattress, two bends in the stairs did not help us, Churchill trying to explain as he puffed. "This was a special customer, mattresses were in short supply, he had made a firm promise."

"I was storing all this information for possible use later. I had at least six customers wanting mattresses. Mrs Stranger wanted two, his customer could not possibly be more 'special' than 'my' Mrs. Stranger. All I ever got was, "They are in short supply, I will tell you when I get one."

We spread the groundsheet over the car roof, laid the mattress on it, then wondered how to secure it. I sent 'Sir' to find rope, he came back with a ball of string. It could be tied through the open windows at the back, but to do the same in front, we had to be in the car first. Half day, all had gone, the town was like a graveyard. Then I spotted a scruffy looking youth, sort of aimlessly heading our way. He was swinging a half hearted kick at anything and everything in his path, a tin, a bottle, a screw of paper. He looked short in the attic, no lights on upstairs, but beggars cannot be choosers. I went to great pains, explaining word for word what we needed. He caught on, but could not tie a knot in a secure fashion. He passed the two string ends to us through the open windows, one holding whilst the other tied, it seemed secure.

We set off up Chesterfield Road at a sedate pace, we both had an arm out of our respective windows, to help hold it. We seemed to be doing alright, a few 'in a hurry' drivers were a bit irate at our slow progress, but we had enough on and ignored them. Then, the car in front signalled his intention to turn left, slowed down to do so. I had to slow down, and then to change down, so I had to use two hands, left the mattress to its own devices for a few seconds. The car behind hooted his frustration, I pressed on the loud pedal. With a 'ping' the string parted, the mattress was torn from its moorings, out of 'sir's' grasp. My eyes shot to the rear view mirror. The mattress bounced on the road once, then went straight over the car behind, the driver ducking instinctively, he looked as though he would shunt me up the rear end. I gave it more loud pedal. The little car has never, before or since, shot away like that. I pulled into the kerb beyond the road junction just as soon as the irate driver had sped past. We both ran back. Churchill was clucking like an irate hen as he dusted it down, looking for tears. In luck, just a few dirty marks, not even a scuff.

Back on top with it, no string, we both clung to it as we continued at almost walking pace. I helped him carry it into the house, then left him to it, and retired to the car for a thoughtful fag. I had learned a lot this day.

A distraught Churchill re appeared. "She spotted the dirty marks."

"Oh dear."

So he had knocked five pounds off the price, then went on. "It doesn't matter really, as I had put five pounds on in the first place." We motored back in silence, I was thinking, 'I've got such a lot to learn.' I don't know what he was thinking.

After dropping him back at the shop, I realised I was still tense, I called round to see Linda, she was in, alone, I told her all. Then we had a half hour doing some practical biology, after which I was more relaxed and went home. A nice tea, all relaxed, Dad came in. "'ave yer sin 'im, is 'ee in?"

"I'm here," I called out, getting out of his chair with alacrity.

He burst through the passage curtain. "Done know wot yer've bin doin, but yer bring no trouble 'ere. Yer've made your own bloody bed. So yer can bloody well lie on it. It's no business of mine, so you can shurrup afore yer start." He hung the dog lead on the front door hook, settled in his chair, rested his head on his right hand, tucked his left hand in his trouser waistband, shut his eyes.

Mum peeped through the curtain, shook her head, looked at me with appeal, limped back to her kitchen domain...

Considering all the rumpus the previous week, the week following was quite reasonable. A few customers had heard rumours, I said there had been an office mix up, whilst wondering how such news had got so far in so little time.

Thursday was a nice bright morning, feeling pretty good I sauntered into the shop just before ten a.m. to be met with...

"S.S. sorry Mr. Ch.Ch. Chapman, we've gone through it all w.w.with a f.f.fine t.t.tooth comb, you do still owe us almost t.t.twenty pounds."

I just stood and looked, that floored me. 'She', stood behind him with a fixed fiendish grin on her dial. A long pregnant pause, whilst I digested. Then I managed to grind out my reply. "Hard bloody lines then, you don't expect me to cough up to clear your incompetent office staff, do you?"

"Th. Th. That's the rules I'm afraid."

'She' was leering backwards from her desk. I think that look pushed me over the edge.

"Well you can stuff your bloody rules, and the bloody job, I'm finished." I stormed back to the car, returned with my ledgers, placed them with great car on 'her' desk in front of 'her'. "Give 'her' the bloody job see how she fares," and walked out to savour that glorious day.

Chapter 14
What Do We Do Now?

I went to the pub, had three pints, unusual, made no comments about Joyce's boobs resting on the bar, very unusual. Did not say a word to anyone. VERY VERY un usual. Deep in thought, I realised that had I thought twice I would not have said that to Churchill, but I had not even thought once and said it.

None of the regulars spoke, they looked with unease at each other, many a one looked at me.

I began to climb to my feet, Walter Joyce, the local 'man from the Pru' came in, navy blue suit, very clean black shoes, very overweight, complete with bowler hat. He pressed with both hands on my shoulders. "Don't get up, I want words with you." Then went to the bar, soon returning with two pints. One he placed before me.

"I've had more than my ration already," I protested.

"You have every right, one question. "Did you go or were you pushed?"

"The bloody bush telegraph around here knows more about me than I do," I chuntered.

"One of the joys of small village life I guess. Walter grinned. "I ask again, did you go or were you pushed?"

"I went."

"Thought as much, family temper?"

The smile took any sting out of the comment. I had to admit, I was only just now beginning to realise just what I really had done.

"Have you thought about what you are going to do now?" I could only shake my head. "Have you thought about starting on your own?"

My hollow laughter must have sounded maniacal. "How, what with? Not a chance matey."

"Do you realise what a good reputation you have?" Then, still grinning added. "Apart from the family temper of course. Does your Dad know yet?"

I almost froze with horror, I had not had time, thought, to even contemplate that frightening problem.

"How much do they pay you?" Almost with a flourish, he magically produced paper and pencil from pockets.

"I thought for a moment, guess over the time on this new round I've must have averaged about nine or ten pounds a week. I bumped into the mechanic from the garage that I used to work under a few weeks ago. He is still on under eight pounds. Gawd, I don't want to return to all that filth."

"No need," from a still smiling Walter. "Any car allowance?"

"Ten bob a week."

"How do they arrive at your wage?"

"Five pounds a week basic, plus one and six in the pound for each pound over fifty."

"Slave labour," was his only comment as his pencil flew over the paper at bewildering speed. Transposing, crossing out, starting again on new columns, he eventually pushed his chair back with a sigh of satisfaction.

"Listen to this, I reckon they must be working on at least a hundred percent mark up, how does your one and six in the pound sound now?"

"You are joking," I blustered.

He shook his head in an emphatic No. "You could buy locally as you want and still make twenty per cent." Then he dropped the bombshell. "I've got a spare five hundred I will put in with you to help you get started."

I just stared, open mouthed, the thought of anybody ever having a 'spare' five hundred was beyond my comprehension. The brain began to catch up. "When would you want it back?"

"I don't, you put five hundred in yourself, then we split the profit fifty fifty at the year end. If you put a thousand in yourself, we split two thirds to a third at year end."

My thoughts were racing. 'He thinks I have five hundred or even a thousand.'

He was speaking again. "No hurry, give it some thought, then drop a note through my letter box when you've decided. Now I have some business to discuss with Freddie." With a friendly pat on my shoulder, he walked over to Freddie.

At home, I sat at the table, head in hands, worried out of my wits. I had already told Mum in the kitchen, she was worried sick. "Don't wake him," she pleaded. "You know his temper if his sleep is disturbed."

News time, Dad stirred, opened one bleary eye and instructed. "Switch t' wireless on."

I obeyed with alacrity, as was expected. The news seemed to go on for ever. When it did end, he motioned that I should switch it off.

As I walked back from the wireless corner, I spoke with a frog in my throat. "Dad, I've er some news to tell you."

"Yer've no cain ter bloody bother, it's all rernd t' bloody pit. I'ts your bloody bed, yer've made it, ner yer can bloody lie on it." He put his boots on, shrugged into his coat, and went out with the dog.

Grunting with pain, Mum struggled up from the kitchen. "How did he take it lad?"

"He already knew."

She sighed, tousled my hair and limped back to her kitchen.

I lit yet another cigarette, a tap on the door, and in walked Bill. Well it should be William, but he with a partner had started an electrical appliance business locally. All the village knew them as Bill & Ben, But within their ear shot it was William and Jack. William was a small gentle chap in his private life. His wife and mother in law ruled him with a rod of iron. But in business, a very hard man. According to all reports, their charges were way above shops in the big town, but as they were the only ones in the village, they seemed to be able to get away with it. In private life, Bill's eyes were gentle, huge bushy eyebrows that were never ever trimmed. Away from his ruling women, a business deal, then the eyes hardened, they then looked like flint, he was a different person.

"Just heard the news, mate," he started. "Have yer thought of going on your own?"

Surprise was not the word, more shell shocked, so many knew, so soon.

"Not really, why?"

"Well if you do, me and my partner will put a

thousand in with you between us."

My brain was in turmoil, how, why, does everybody want to get 'in on the act'. If ever there is an act. We were still discussing the pros and cons when Dad got back.

"Been as yer not werking, yer can take me to Bellaugh for some plants termorrer." He settled in his chair, and his eyes closed.

Bill and I went outside. "Can I sleep on it?" I asked.

"Sawright, call in the shop to say when you've decided."

Very little sleep that night, I was well and truly bed raggled as I stumbled down stairs to answer the harshly ringing phone. Bemused, the message hardly registered. It was Eric. "You must meet me in the Hare and hounds tonight at seven thirty, these are instructions." The phone went dead.

The dog and I had a long walk, no lunch, we sat on fences and thought, sat on logs and mused. The old girl listened to everything I had to say, I'm sure she understood. If I had never smoked, or had the occasional drink, spent on the car, I could never ever have had what others seemed to look on as 'spare'. My 'tackle' was still painful, I looked when easing myself, it was now a sort of purple black with yellow streaks. With a rueful grin, I realised that the only time it did not hurt so much was when Linda was saying, "Sorry," and kissing it better. Possibly that is the 'Hair of the dog?' I decided to sit again, this time on a 'proper' seat at the side of Churm's Lane. Head back, eyes closed, my reverie was disturbed by a flurry of noise. A small 'Sheltie' was showing interest in Scamp's rear end. Scamp was giving a deep throated warning. Worried for its welfare I looked around for the owner. Then a voice from the path behind me.

"Aye up me duck. You're still in trouble then"? Dot English, Bill Priest's near neighbour, looking very smart. A full pleated skirt, with matching blouse, an open zip golfing jacket, brogue shoes.

"You look very nice, have you lost weight?"

"Thank you, kind sir," with a slight dip of the knee before joining me on the seat. "If you must know, I have a new girdle and a new bra. I know where the inches have gone, you will have to guess where." She was chuckling at her own honesty. "I'm still a very good listener, and a curer of pain, you're still in both lots of trouble aren't you?"

"Thank you for your interest, but I do not think that I should trouble you, In any case, we don't really know each other well enough do we?"

I think that must have hurt, she looked taken aback. "Listen lad, when you've been around as much as I have, you learn that in life you meet a few people that you know are right for you. It's not very often, it's special, your one. I want to help you with your pain and worries if I possibly can."

So, haltingly, with plenty of cigarettes, I brought her up to date, she was disgusted with my treatment, delighted at offers of help I had hinted at, then pointed out if 'others' thought I was worthy of such trust, I should have more faith in myself.

She ground out her cigarette end under her heel, took a deep breath looked deep into my eyes, and said. "Now that's almost sorted, let's attend to your wedding tackle.

143

Don't start iffing and butting, in all my nursing experience, my married life, and help with pit accidents I have attended to. I've seen more tassles than you've had hot dinners. My husband and his brother work in the pit stores, lots of heavy lifting. All men seem to drop weight on their wrong bits. Far better to see me than have the ambulance staff laughing and telling all the pit. They all trust me to keep quiet and are more than satisfied with the results. Get in this field behind us, then am I getting it out or are you?"

"But it's very personal."

"So's pain lad, come on in to the field."

She all but dragged me up the path behind, through a gap in the hedge by an old oak. I tried to ease my backside to save catching it, and brought the pitiful, painful, bit into view. "That's nice," with a note of approval. "You've over half a pound of meat there, somebody has given it a real tousing, and I don't suppose for a minute that it was you? That's not for my ears lad, but all that meat does not want to be in 'Y' fronts, that needs boxer shorts."

"I've tried them, but it all drops down the leg."

"I'm not at all surprised," with a pleased grin. Then she dug in her hand bag. 'Dug in' was right, the stuff she got out of it. Combs powder, lipstick, various pills, change, letters, sun specs, pens, pencils. Right at the bottom, a battered ointment tin. Handing it over, she instructed. "Smear it all over with this, or would you rather me do it for you?"

I turned my back and did as instructed. It was almost magical, within seconds most of the pain, well, just

144

went.

I made myself respectable, and turned, to give her the tin back with thanks. "Keep it, I have plenty more, smear it night and morning, in no time it will be as good as new. Bring it up on Saturday afternoon so that I can make sure all is well." She was almost looking coy.

We wandered back to the seat, sat, and lit up. "Oh yes," she started. I waited. "The speedy bush telegraph, how the news gets here so quickly, I've got it sorted. Your 'Fussy Breeches' has an aunt in our village, you may know her, lives down the old part. A Mrs. Rightwell, bright red hair, husband a foreman on the pit top, when they made him foreman, they paid to put him the phone in so that they could call him out at all hours."

Just like that, it sounded complicated, but all logical, fussy breeches could have phoned her aunt within seconds of any news breaking, she told her husband, and he passed it round the pit. I thought about it all then asked "What is in the ointment? It's good."

"I don't know, Fred Parker the Chemist makes it up for me, he varies the ingredients to suit the injury. I know he uses honey, glycerine, almond oil, liquid paraffin and Oh.!" She burst out laughing. "That mix has a lot of calamine in it, a chap at t' pit burnt his with a welding torch. It will have a crust on it in the morning." We both had to laugh at the thought.

She looked at me intently. "Do you like jokes?"

"Yes, why?"

"It's not a joke, but it's as good as. While I was at the hospital we lost one, sad, but it happens all too often. You blokes are all so worried about the size of what you have (not important in fact). If ever there was a good one in the morgue, all were invited in to look. This one was really special, if he had served in the middle east he could never have worn shorts. We were all very impressed apart from the old man who used to sweep the mortuary out, we had to ask him why."

His reply. "It's nothing like as big as mine, but it's just as bloody dead."

We walked back up the lane together, well sauntered really, chatted about anything and everything. Then I remembered Dad's orders yesterday about his trip to Bellaugh for garden plants. I quickly explained, and made to rush off. She put her hand on my arm. "If you do start on your own, we will trade with you, cash only, but it will all help."

Dad already had boots, cap, and jacket on. "Yer've left it plenty late enough, if Joe Weymouth is 'avin' 'is tea yer'll 'ear frum me."

I just had time to spread the groundsheet on the back seat, fat old Scamp was in. She was overweight, slow, old, but was always available for a trip out.

Dad spent the whole journey bleating about how late it was, plus threats if the 'plant man' had closed down. I urged the little car on at top speed. The village green was bathed in evening sunlight, the Maypole was freshly painted, all a picture of English tranquillity. Joe was beginning to take his boxes of plants in. Another village handyman, he could tackle almost everything, small, very portly. Age? He could have been anything between fifty five and seventy five. He greeted Dad with nonchalant indifference.

"Not sin yer fer a while Mister, wer'es your car?"

Dad explained that he had to stop driving. "I've 'ad ter get 'im ter bring me." Nodding towards me.

Then I saw a large buck rabbit grazing by the Maypole. "I'll put Scamp back in the car."

"Done bother."

"But that rabbit, it's tame, it's someone's pet."

"I said done bother, she ant 'ad a rabbit fer ages."

"That's my pet buck," from Joe.

"My dog eats rabbits whole." from Dad.

"That rabbit 'as lived all its life on this green." From Joe.

"Gerron," Dad instructed Scamp.

I was transfixed with horror, whilst fat old Scamp could not believe her luck. she was struggling to run, but I'm sure she had a smile on her face.

The rabbit stopped grazing, and watched her approach warily. Scamp was almost on it, when the rabbit spun on its front feet, and lashed out with both back legs, kicking Scamp really hard under the jaw. She yelped with either pain or surprise, and watched with the most comical expression on her face as the rabbit scurried towards Joe and leapt into his arms.

"Yer keep yer munny, an' I'll keep me plants." Joe instructed as he took the rabbit indoors.

Dad was livid, with a stream of abuse he clambered back into the passenger's seat. I opened the back door for a bemused Scamp to get in.

"Tek me omm." Dad instructed. We never spoke a word all the way back, and as far as I know Dad never ever spoke to Joe again.

Scamp died in her sleep that night, at almost nineteen years of age and so fat, hardly surprising, but Dad will always blame Joe.

I had to sob silent tears, Dad would have gone spare to see anyone cry. In bed, out driving, I, many times, had to pull into the side to wipe my eyes to clear my vision. What a friend she had been for all those years. She always greeted me, sneezing with pleasure, she always sat and listened whilst I told her of my problems. When I went out to meet a girl, I had to walk Scamp as an excuse, otherwise I was not allowed out at night. She would sit uncomplaining for ages whilst we kissed and cuddled. She had seen me off when I joined up, and again when I went to India. I had only been a young schoolboy when Dad and I had fetched her from near Southport. Dad had an old army pal, then a farm manager near Formby, he had fallen and damaged his back, no good as a farm manager, so the owner had sacked him. A tied cottage, he had to get out. Southport council had offered him a council house, but the rule was, 'NO DOGS'. He had written to Dad to explain all with a P.S. "We move on Monday, I will shoot Scamp Sunday."

Dad had sent a Telegram straight back. "Don't shoot, we will collect Sunday." Now I was at the 'wrong' end of my twenties. Such a trusted friend can never be replaced, yet I dare not show my grief. Dad would dismiss me as a sniveller, no back bone. Once I was sobbing in our toilet, I don't know for how long. Dad's voice outside. "Ow much longer are yer gooin' to be in theer?" Now, in possibly my worst ever situation she was not here to listen.

It got worse the next morning a short letter from Linda.

"Dear Ron, Sorry I have to write like this, we have loads of problems, the worst, Reg, my brother in law has dropped dead at the pit. We are all devastated. All in a rush, the rest of us are moving to Lincolnshire this weekend straight after the funeral. 'He', is off work again, all screaming and shouting at each other, I can't get away quick enough. DON'T call or write, it would make it all worse. I will write or phone as soon as I can. PLEASE obey and trust me.
Yours (as always) Linda"

I walk out of a job, my dog dies, now this. But why such a rushed move? "Oh why oh why?" Then, almost realisation, I was in love with another man's wife. I drove out to Dubdy common, sat and smoked, cried, smoked some more. Then drove back to the Church car park. Looked in the driving mirror, I looked ninety. I jogged round the football pitch to try and get some colour in my cheeks, all it did was make me out of breath, and look even worse. I swilled my face in the Dam, and dried it on the dog towel. Need I say more?

Chapter 15
If You Could Live Your Life All Over Again And Did The Same Things That You Have Done, You Would Finish Up Just Where You Are Now.

Just in time, I remembered Eric's instructions about the Hare & Hounds tonight. I did not want to go, I did not want company at all, all I wanted to do was stew in my own misery. But through it all I realised that if I did not turn up, he would come hunting for me. I washed, changed, and shaved, as I walked across the Hare car park, a beaming Eric came to meet me. He shook me firmly by the hand which I felt was very strange.

"Many thanks for your help with the Ma in Law. If that parcel had not been here for Sunday I would have been forever in the dog house. I am beyond help, a womaniser and a drunkard. She should know about drunks, her husband is past caring every night. It's no good trying to tell her about bad cars, she's so thick. Once I was daft enough to take her to Scotland in the little caravan. As we passed Loch Ness, I said that this was the Loch they 'thought' might hold a monster.

"Is there one?" she asked.

I said, "No one knew it was so deep."

"Why don't they dip a telegraph pole in it to find out how deep it is?"

I looked to see if he was kidding, he was not!

We put the van on a site outside a hotel at Aviemore, went in for a drink. Whilst I was ordering someone asked her. "Was she in a caravan, or staying at the hotel?"

"I don't know," she ses, "You will have to ask my

son in law."

Then I realised how bad things were for him.

Undeterred, he went on. "Her headaches are 'special'. When she gets one, she wears her husband's cap, plus sun specs, but has the wireless on. Do you now realise why I can't explain about coils burning out or Hardy Spicer joints faulty?"

"If the joints are so bad why don't you carry a spare?"

"That shows how out of date you are, no joints can be replaced, it means a new prop shaft every time. Ford fit six different ones, all garages seem to stock the five I don't want, but never the one I do. We all do well over fifty thousand miles a year, so the cars are replaced yearly, they're getting to be pretty well clapped out by then. Anyway, most folk will be here by now, come on in."

I was dragged in, still not sure, still not knowing a thing.

Early as it was, the Red Room was bursting at the seams, a haze of smoke and a gabble of noise greeted as he opened the door and walked in. Almost a sort of cheer went up.

"Thank you all for coming, with special thanks to my mate here who made it all possible. Get your first drinks on me." He turned, half hugged me, and shook my hand yet again, and rushed to the bar.

I just stood like tripe, looked around, all were familiar, most school and pre school friends. Quite a few were pushing forward to say hello. Eric forced his way through them already with two foaming pints. He passed one over. "All due to you mate, with very many thanks."

I did not know what to say or do. "But what, why?" I began to question.

"I have passed the exam mate, all thanks to you, plus, I have also won the award for the best presented paper of the year." At last, light dawned, I was so pleased for him. I may have had a small tear welling, I'm sure he had, we winked at each other whilst we supped, with pleased grins.

"I'm so pleased for you, I just do not know what to say."

"Say nowt, and give us yer pot." He sped towards the bar again.

I was grinning foolishly at his back, thinking that now was not the time to try and curb his drinking. A hand gripped my upper arm, a voice in my ear. "Now then sir, have I your permission to speak sir?"

So pleased to hear again that once familiar voice. Arthur Maurice (Mog) a mate from way back as far as very early school days. Tall, slim, good looking, dark wavy hair, always smart, usually dressed in navy blue, a superb sense of humour. Not been seen around for some time, rumour had it that he was now working for a West Midlands brewery as a sales rep, was in fact now living in the West Midlands. Delighted to see him I shook his hand firmly and asked what he was doing here.

"I have come to see my brothers and my Mother. It would seem that I am lucky, seeing you and just in time for some celebration or other. Do tell me. "What are we celebrating?"

I quickly explained regards Eric's job, his difficulties

exam wise, and the happy results. Eric arrived back, gave one of the pints to Mog, and returned to replenish his own.

Mog then told me that he could join in the 'supping', as his firm had already put him forward as a trainee sales manager. Eric just got back in time to hear this, more smiles and hand shakes. All this had taken my own problems out of my mind for a while, but looking around I began to realise how everyone was so happy, but me.

"I have a new 'funny' for you," Eric started. "The true ones are always the best. A few days after I had taken the exam, a customer's neighbour asked me to look at her little lad, he had gone deaf in one ear and it was hurting him. I suggested the hospital as the best route. This seemed to please the little lad and frighten his Mum. Would I please take him? I said not possible, but she pleaded, husband at work, three more little ones, she was tied. So I did. On the way there he told me that has brother had recently been in hospital for a tonsillectomy, three whole days with nothing to eat but ice cream. That explained his keenness. The E.N.T. Spec. knew me, so we went almost straight in. He was simply ages 'firtling' in the little chap's ear before 'ping', and into the kidney tray dropped an almost perfectly round white, pebble.

"Now how did that get in your ear?" The specialist asked as he dropped the pebble into the small waiting hand."

"Seasy," from the lad, as he flirted it back in his ear again. "I feared I was going to be witness to a murder, it took him another twenty minutes with a syringe to get it out again."

Mog took over. "We have made friends with our local fish shop owners, they're Pakistanis, but very nice people. We've had a meal with them, and invited them back, but the very day they were due, our little girl developed Chicken Pox. Too late to put them off, we met them at the door to explain."

"Have either of you ever had Chicken Pox? Then reverting into a superb Bombay Welsh accent, Mog delivered his punch line.

"Oh No, Mr Maurice, we have not the Chicken Pox had, but we are very, very sure that it will be very, very nice."

A rumpus by the door, we all looked up, Burly Bert was forcing his way through the crowd, he arrived, red faced, flushed with success. "A little lad," he announced with some pride.

Amidst the back slapping, I pointed out. "I dare not mention it, you haven't. It's well over a year now since you thought she might be."

He gave an embarrassed sort of smile before answering. "She's in the record books for attending Peel Street fifteen months for the same pregnancy. When they said she was she couldn't have been, then when they didn't know she must 'ave been. I've been visiting every night this week, but our Mae has gone tonight, she's coming here after. It seems a lot have cause to celebrate tonight."

I had a quiet mutter. "Apart from me."

Bert was looking towards the door. "She's here now."

A bewildered, questioning, almost frightened Mae's face was peering round the door.

"She's never ever bin in a pub in 'er life afore," Bert explained.

He raised both his arms aloft. Relief spread over Mae's face when she saw him, she began to move through the crowd, followed by about the thinnest, tallest, weed of a youth I have ever seen. His skin colour was rather like 'gone off' suet, then to enhance it all, he had a little daft wisp of a 'going to be one day' moustache on his upper lip.

Mog gripped my arm, mouthed into my ear. "He looks as though he's spent all winter in the garden, under a bucket with the rhubarb." A typical Mog humorous summing up, I realised through my chuckles.

Mae went up to Bert, whispered in his ear, he beamed with pleasure. She then came to me, a full blooded kiss, full on the mouth, then whispered to me. "Glad you're not mad with me, you've missed the boat, but I still intend to have you one day."

My pleased smile beginning to develop, just froze.

Eric called across the crowded heads. "Mog, Ron once told me that you and he whilst at school were instructed by the head to wipe graffiti off the toilet walls. You were the only two clean minded boys in the school. Is it another of his yarns?"

Mog's head went back with a bellow of laughter, really showing his two prominent front teeth. "Yes, he had us up in assembly in front of the whole school. An example of clean minded youth, he called us. The school was in uproar, they all knew we had the best collection of smutty jokes between us. Poor 'Pecker', I wonder if he ever realised the truth?"

It was all beginning to wind down now. I positioned myself near the door and took ten bob each off them all for the drinks kitty, a few demurred, till I snarled at them. Joyce would re distribute to the ones who had done all the paying out. I just knew it had all been Eric, Mog, and Bert.

Mae had been gone for some time. She had been for a goodnight kiss, complete with the promise or threat of future delights in store for me. Before shooting off with the boy friend to do whatever they had in mind.

I had been drinking strongly, but felt detached and very sober. I went to the Gent's, stood steaming and thinking. Dot's ointment really had worked wonders, all was pristine yet again. I settled on a seat by the Red Room door, jammed it open, fresh air pouring in, nice. A lot had gone, the ones left were feeling no pain, heading with determination in their tread for the outside world. I looked up. The three musketeers were heading my way with purposeful treads.

"We've only just heard," from Mog.

"What will you do?" from Bert. Eric, just very thoughtful.

They all pulled up chairs to almost surround me, nothing short of a gabble, till Eric took charge.

"Now is not the time chaps, no one is thinking clearly, it can all be sorted, but let's leave it till the brains are clear, be best if we all went home now."

Chapter 16
Time For Serious Thought

The next morning with a mouth like a baby's pram. (All pee and biscuits) I sat, and looked at my breakfast, without any real interest. Mum had put the wireless on, they had just mentioned the weather. "The whole area will be dry today, but some isolated parts may get rain." Typical of these days. Dot England had told me recently that she had applied for a phone to be installed, 'They' had written to her. The letter said. "Our engineers will call a week on Monday to fit your telephone. If you don't get this letter, would you please be good enough to phone the number above to confirm that this date will be suitable?" Either me or this world is going crazy I decided.

Mum limped up from the kitchen, put an arm round my shoulders. "Have you decided what to do yet lad?"

"Afraid not Mum, my mind is so bewildered, it's not working."

She gave that soft, uncertain smile, that was a speciality of hers. "Your Aunt Ethel called yesterday, she says that Uncle Bob will lend you a thousand at two and a half percent interest if you do decide to have a go on your own."

"Whew, that's a lot of money, where has he got it from? When would he want it back? It would take simply ages to pay all that back." All that gabbled without a pause.

"Don't forget her dress making, two incomes, they don't eat like us, they have never run a car, Ethel will walk round town all day to save a halfpenny on a card of buttons, even if it costs her two pence in shoe leather, but think lad, I would rather you owe Bob money than any business man." She gave 'that' smile again, and hobbled back down the passage.

I just sat, thought, and realised for the first time, just how sensible she was.

Still 'awa with the fairies', a knock on the front door brought me to earth with a jolt. It was a bleary eyed Eric. "I know it's difficult for us to think straight, but think we must. I've got the dog, come, let's walk."

I went down to the kitchen to tell Mum where we were going.

We started walking like two elderly Gents, both quiet, the dog sniffing at anything and everything that took its fancy. I tried to push Scamp and Linda out of my mind, difficult, but it must be done.

Then, as the fresh air began to get to the parts that nothing else could reach, without realising, we began to walk in a more airman like manner, the backs straightened, the stride lengthened.

"This is what we both needed," I just nodded, walked, and thought.

"Have you realised, with all this financial support, you can start without any money of your own?"

"Yes, but."

"That's the 'but' I want to talk to you about."

"Mum made me realise this morning, I would not be working for myself. There's now another offer in the pipeline, from a relative, at two and a half percent interest. No profit sharing."

"That sounds a lot better," from a highly pleased Eric. "Now listen, and listen hard. This should have been said earlier, but my selfish mind was all on swotting. I should have warned you before. When you work for the big boys, you work your balls off for a pittance. 'The Firm', always sees to it that they win in every possible way. It's a short cut to a dicky heart or a breakdown, all fer nowt. Work for yourself, you never have any money in your pocket, the customers have it in their homes, you still get the breakdown, but when and if you get it, the money is yours. I never could, but I think that you are a stronger person than I."

I gave him a quizzical look, I did not believe that.

"S'right, all that you need do, is insist on getting a shilling in the pound each week off your own, hand picked customers. You'll finish up with a reputation like Bill, but you'll have a good business. You need to be hard, they all become good friends, they are reliable and regular, you let the rules slide, then before you realise, your book debt is sky high, takings don't move, so that you can't afford to take more out. If you think that you can handle it, I will take you round some suppliers, tomorrow if you like."

I was really moved. "But what about your own job, your firm?"

"Nae bother, I phoned this morning, explained I would not be fit for work today, I told them all about you and your help, in fact they all but suggested it. I must have done a good job, they have offered you work with us, selling hearing aids."

I was busy looking at him in astonishment, tripped

over a tree root, and went all my length.

Eric pulled me to my feet, explaining through laughter. "Remember lad, when one door shuts, another one slams in your face."

"But I don't have," I started.

"I know you don't have, but all these others must have faith in you, reckon the least that you can do is have a bit in yourself."

He let me stew in my own juice, whilst we walked in silence. Up Clipsham old drive, down by the old well, along the field side, over a farm gate, he reminded me that we used to jump over that same gate fifteen or so years ago, 'no way' now. It was well over five feet high. Over the railway bridge, past the sewage works, then left into Churms Lane. We approached the seat of my most embarrassing moment.

Eric nodded towards it. "I don't know about you, but I'm ready for a sit and a fag." I burst out laughing.

"What's so funny?" As we lit cigarettes, I pondered, 'do I tell him'?

"Aw, what the L, we've been good mates for years. So I told him, recounted all that happened during those fateful days, no names of course, finishing with the special treatment from that special Lady, at this very same place.

Eric's face was a picture, every possible expression showed, horror, disbelief, amusement. He almost howled with laughter. Then I saw the Sheltie, too late, she was speaking.

"My, that must be a good one, please tell me. Hello Eric, I did not realise that you two knew each other."

"Hello Mrs. England, yes, we go back a long long way, but not as far back as you and I."

That would be difficult, it was I who nursed you after circumcision."

Eric was almost blushing as he explained. "This is the lady you should have consulted for your treatment, she really is the 'tackle' expert."

The look on my face gave it all away, we all burst out laughing.

When we recovered, she asked. "Do either of you know Mrs. Priest's sister?"

I shook my head, Eric nodded, whilst she went on. "I think she must have had an accident, she was wearing a head scarf this morning, but it could not hide the best black eye that I have ever seen."

"Should I know her?" I asked.

"Not if you've any sense, she and her sister are without doubt the worst two payers for miles. Her name is Swift, she lives in the colliery village."

I think that my eyes must have sort of glazed over.

"You do know her."

I explained what I had done. Both thought it was what Billie Bunter would have called "A spiffing wheeze."

Chapter 18
The Start Of A New Era

Eric took me to the big City in the morning, talk about an eye opener, I soon realised that my education had not even started. General warehouse, bespoke wear, furniture, hardware, ironmongery, even garden furniture. All would offer me a hundred pounds worth of credit a month, until I had proved my worth, then the sky was the limit. All gave a two and a half percent discount for prompt payment at month end, some went as high as three and a half. None would hear of me using a mark up of less than twenty five percent, some advocated at least thirty. It was all beginning to look so easy. We even found a kitchen suite for Claire. A warm honey woodwork, with bronze seat pads. I just knew it would be right for her. It looked real quality. Eric insisted that we should get it delivered direct, now this minute. I was scared to make the plunge. So he paid cash and put three and a half percent in his pocket. "My gain, your loss," he grinned. "If it's Edna's sister, it's safe, pay me when she pays you. I bet you ten bob we get it within a week."

Driving back home, I never said a word, my mind was on cloud nine, it all seemed so easy. Eric nattered all the time, most, I did not hear or take in. Till he said. "Have you anywhere to keep your stock?"

"No need, I can get it as I want it."

"What about splitting dozens?"

"They will, but they'll charge extra, some as much as twenty percent. Begin to think and add up. Pants, vests, all boxed in dozens, you need at least seven sizes, underskirts, blouses, jumpers, shirts, do you need me to go on?"

All my joy deflated like a pricked balloon. I must be an idiot.

Leave it with me, I will have a word with widow Wells on our Street corner, she has four bedrooms, and now lives alone." Then added, "Apart from when her boozing gambling son returns to roost." He dropped me off at home after a playful punch on the jaw. I walked in, on high, all would soon be well.

Mum called out just as soon as I got in. "There's a letter for you on the mantle piece. I strolled over and opened it. The heading. Sydney S. Solomons, General Warehousemen.

"Dear Sir,

You are hereby informed that following your dismissal from the above firm The Contract of Employment you signed originally, states categorically that you are not allowed to offer your services to any other similar firm for a period of ten years and within a radius of twenty miles from any branch of ours that employed you." Signed Sydney S. Solomons

I just dropped into Dad's chair, drained of action, colour, everything.

Mum's face came through the curtain. "What's up lad?"

I passed the letter to her.

She scanned it. "What's it mean then?"

"It means that they're liars, I was not sacked, I walked out, but the rest means that I can't work this area.

The branch I started at is over twenty miles away, but the one I was in recently is only six."

"But they can't do that."

"It looks as though they can and have." Then in a rush, I added. "I'm going to see Eric again." Through the back door, car out of garage, I tore off.

Eric was not fazed at all. "They all do that," he grinned. Leave it with me, I will ring the wife's Uncle, He's an M.P. Have a fag. He dropped a pack and lighter on my knee and went through to the other room.

I ignored the cigarettes, from being on high, I was now in deep despair again. Eric's voice carried through very clear. He said yes three times, no once, then passed on my name address and phone number. Then the laugh crept back in his voice. "Yes he is, yes I will, thank you very much." He came back to me. "Uncle George says not to worry, gerroffom, he will ring you. My meal is ready." He pushed me out of the door.

I sat sort of draped, in the car seat, but legs still trailing out. I could feel tears of frustration pricking the backs of my eyes. Took cigarettes out, then put them back in my pocket. Can't afford, no income, in any case my mouth tasted like a bucket of sawdust. No money, no job, no Scamp, no Linda, now this, would it never end? My self punishment was interrupted.

"Ant yer gorren 'ome ter goo to then?" Dot England's worried face popped round the car door. "Wot yer dun, lost a dollar an' fun a tanner?"

My lack of any response had her worried, she walked round, got into the passenger seat and instructed. "Tek me omm."

164

In a daze, I followed her instructions. Pulled up outside her house. "Lock it and come in." I did.

She made and poured tea, told two jokes, asked how my tassel was, had it got a crust on it? No reaction at all from me, I was impervious to everything.

She then tried a different tack. "Were we not now good enough friends to exchange problems?"

"You have no problems."

"We all have lad, some are for sharing, some not, specials are for special friends only. Really bad ones have to be stored."

"Mine was bad enough, but you wormed it out of me."

"Much worse," she mused it only, with a far away look.

I began to realise, she was watching me closely, long and hard, her eyes were sort of boring through the silence. Then, as if on impulse, she got up, went to an inglenook cupboard the other side of the fireplace, and came back with a full bottle of Gordon's gin. "In your tea or in a glass?"

"But it's hardly tea time," I objected.

"Tea time, dinner time, drink is for the right time in the right company, it's right now, tea or glass?"

Gin is not, and never was my tipple, in tea did not appeal at all, but I said that I would accept a very small one, with tonic if at all possible.

She produced a whisky glass and almost filled it, then managed to get almost a half inch of tonic on top. She then 'topped up' her almost empty tea cup, drank half, filled it up again. "Tell me all." Whilst I tried to get my brain in gear, she explained. "Hubby bought me this bottle a lot of Christmas's ago, I've never felt like it till now. I'm waiting." She topped up her cup again as with my glass.

"Steady on," I warned. "You will have us both under the table."

"Ash long ash I'm under something or somebody I don't really care," speech already slurring. "Let'sh hear your latest."

I filled her in about Eric taking me to the suppliers, my high, then about the letter.

"Tell Eric, he's been though all this many times."

"I just have, he says not to worry."

"Well don't worry, he knows." Then she lapsed into silence, what was she thinking? Or was it the gin? I gave us both cigarettes and lit them, still silence.

"Can I help?"

The question seemed to snap her reverie. But still, almost in a trance, she topped up both our vessels, then mumbled. "Yes, I think you are the one to tell."

"They tell me that I'm a very good listener," I quoted her line and almost smiled. That seemed to bring her back to earth. Almost mechanically, she started to speak.

"I will not ask for your silence, I just know I will get it, listen to two long tragic stories. When I was nursing, we had a very bad case from a Smeeton pit. It was during the change over from colliers to power coal cutters. A big strong lad, early twenties was admitted, a good amateur boxer I believe. The coal cutter had jammed, it was switched off whilst he went round to the blades to clear the obstruction. The deputy switched the machine on

166

again. It took both his hands off, just above the wrists."

I visibly winced, I had seen Dad's various accidents, broken back, crushed foot, both legs broken, but nothing as tragic as this.

She noticed, and nodded her understanding. "Terrible," she admitted. "He was a big strong healthy lad, he recovered well. I had to give him a blanket bath every morning, as he got better, so did his feelings. Every morning when I touched him, he got a tremendous hard on, he was in agony. I could not stand his situation, one morning I just had to help relieve him. I was rubbing it for him, Y'know what I mean? Matron came round the screens and caught me doing it. I was sacked instantly. All was kept quiet, which thinking back might have made it worse. I've never really got over it."

I was stunned, as I managed to digest, and absorb.

"There's more," she went on. "Almost two years ago, my husband and three of his mates had to move a big heavy motor. The crane had put it in the wrong place, it had rolled to where the crane could not be used again. It was far too big for the four of them, but it just had to be moved. They were all heaving and straining, one slipped, hubby got more weight than ever, it did his back in, caused a hernia, worst of all, his 'bits' have never worked since. Suspect that 'pussy' might have healed up by now. He's seen the specialist many times, he says it was caused by a loss of blood for a while. IF the blood supply does get working again, all will be well, if not, it will never work again. It's all in the lap of the Gods. All we can do is wait and see. Dad knows how much I used to like 'it' and told me that if I ever need a man, he does not really mind, as long as he does not know about it."

Her eyes were filling with tears, I leaned forward to take her hand. "You poor Dear," was all I could think of to say. That did it, tears arrived in a flood. I stood and took her now shaking shoulders in my arms, her head rested on my shoulder, she sobbed and sobbed, her whole body racked with spasms, she shook with grief, the tears literally poured, heart broken.

Just how long we stood like that, I can't say. Eventually the sobs became less frequent, as did the shakes. She leaned back, groping for a hanky, I passed the inevitable 'spare'. She wiped her eyes, then looked at me with horror. "Just look at what I've done to you," she gasped. I looked down, and realised the cause of her concern. My coat and shirt were drenched, it looked as though someone had been throwing buckets of water at me. Mopping at her reddened bleary eyes, she instructed. "Tek em off lad, yer Muther will wonder what yer've bin up to."

I shed my jacket, she rushed off with it, "on a hanger in the airing cupboard," she muttered as she rushed past. Back she came, ironing board, and iron at the ready. "Shirt," as she erected the board and plugged the iron in. "Vest as well," as that also soggy garment was revealed. She wet a finger, put it on the iron sole plate, "Needs a few more minutes," and filled us up with gin yet again, cup and glass.

Now I was standing, rocking, I think? Never have been a gin drinker, I was almost morbid, even though the mind was blank. She set about the ironing as though the end of the world was nigh. That was all I could register, I still stood, rocked, and tried to think. She was almost a blur as she rushed, shirt on a hanger on the mantle piece in front of the fire, the vest actually sizzled as she offered the hot iron to it. In no time at all, that was joining the shirt. She switched the iron off.

"You poor dear," I murmured, as she tried to stand after bending down to switch off at the power point. I lifted her to her feet, kissed her gently in the centre of her forehead. Her hands were on my shoulders, she looked into my eyes, and said "I think you're the one."

"I'm the one what?" I was about to try and say. But her left arm circled my neck, the right hand stroked my chest, a long lingering kiss followed by another murmur.

"A nice hairy chest," then the right hand started its sure certain slow progress downwards, over my stomach, I sucked it in, the hand carried on, past my waistband under the band of my pants till she found 'it'. "I told you that it would be nice and soft."

It was, soft, small yes, but very very soft, not a spark. No response whatever. My whole body felt similar, but I slowly realised that some how or other I was almost supporting her whole weight. "Can I please use your toilet?" I asked.

With a peculiar look, she said "Yes of course," released me and stood back. We just looked at each other, till with a start she realised I did not know where it was, she told me where to find it. (The loo that is)

I stood gazing into the bowl like narcissus, mind blank, but with a small realisation that I was on dodgy ground. 'It', showed no interest at all, in anything, just small, limp, and lifeless.

After fastening up, I returned to her in the kitchen. Fighting back tears, she questioned. "You don't find me of interest?"

"Oh yes I do, I think that your very attractive."

"I bet you have me down as a real old scrubber."

"Not at all, I really do value your friendship, you're a dishy lady, but Shakespeare is right." Her blank look told me she had no idea what I was talking about. "He wrote, alcohol produces the desire, but ruins the ability. I'm now very sure that he was right."

I began to dress, she just stood and watched, when the time was right she brought my jacket from the airing cupboard, I put it on. "I think I should go now." She just nodded, I turned to the door, looked back with a slight semblance of a wave, she fluttered her fingers in return, tears were very close, I went as quick as I dare.

I had to sit and gather everything in the car before I dare even start to move. Then drove with very great care back home.

I garaged the car and walked in through the back door. Mum's greeting "The shop has phoned, they want you to ring them back."

"Why should I?" I almost snarled at her.

"I think you should," so I did.

Mr. Churchill was full of apologies, the letter was nothing to do with him, it had come straight from head office, he had only just got his copy in the afternoon post. He had telephoned head office to protest, they told him that it was no concern of his, it was their company policy, that was what they always did.

Loads of tutt tutts repeats, more tutt tutts, ending

with, would I please accept his humble apologies? I listened to his tirade in complete silence. It must have been the gin.

When 'Sir' had finished, I told him that I had already made contact with an M.P., I suggested that he might re double his efforts, then with almost a wry smile I finished with Clare's line. "I leave it with you."

Feeling well and truly shattered, I flopped into Dad's chair. The phone had me hoisting myself back on my feet within moments. Not feeling up to the mark I answered "Chapman here."

"Hello Ron, I'm Eric's Uncle in Law." He had a chuckle in his voice and sounded very nice. " Eric asked for advice on your behalf, I've had a word with Sir Hartley Shawcross, we can't get a deal higher. The situation is as follows…

Providing that you do not approach, or solicit any business from their customers, no court in the land would allow any person to be deprived of working for a living in their chosen field. If it did ever get to the 'nitty gritty' you might need to employ a solicitor. But they will know that what I have said is fact, and unless they have proof of you soliciting trade from them, they would lose the case and have to pay costs. However, if you did approach or solicit in any way, it could not only cost you a packet, plus a probability that you may never ever get another job in a similar field. Have you understood all that?"

I thanked him as effusively as I could, plus appreciation of his efforts on my behalf. Not by any means finished yet, he went on. He was only too pleased to help, gave his phone number, address, and assured me that any time I thought I might need help or advice, I need just ring or write, he would do his very best for me. He then went on with a comment that had me thinking long and hard. "Remember, a good reputation takes many years of hard work to attain, but it can be lost in minutes."

I was repeating this to myself as I went down the passage to report the latest to Mum. Then very early to bed. It had been a very harrowing day.

Still asleep, late in the morning the phone woke me. I waited for Mum to answer, she didn't, so I got up and staggered downstairs. No sign of Mum or shopping coat. I picked the instrument up, mumbled "two six one Chapman speaking."

It was a very bright and breezy Mr Churchill, full of confidence, not a trace of stutter. "I phoned the personnel manager at his home last night. He insisted the letters are from head office, company policy, it will not change. The shop is different, that is mine, to run it as I think fit, I told him what a good traveller you are, he thinks the best way out is to ask you to come back to work here. Will you do that?" A slight hesitation, I think he might have been swallowing his own Adam's Apple. "It would save problems in every way if you did."

My mind, always inactive first thing in the morning, plus the gin yesterday, was struggling, working hard to absorb and understand. Facts began to filter through my brain haze. "What about the money you say I owe?"

"Oh, I can scrub that, we get a percentage allowance to strike off bad debts."

I almost had to gasp out aloud. "The bloody rules can

change in minutes." But I managed to keep quiet. "Can I have it in writing that I do not owe you any money?"

The happy man rushed to assure me. Such a letter would be in post this very day. But would I let him know as soon as possible? He was finding it very difficult to replace me.

"Another favour, if I may ask?"

"Yes, what is it?"

"Can you, will you, keep 'Fussy Breeches' out of my hair?"

"Oh, I don't think she will be back, we had a small 'Contre Temps' last night, she stormed out doing the typical distraught female act. Miss Cookson thinks that she is pregnant, the boy that she is engaged to is insisting it's not his. All I know is some nights after work she has been picked up in a car by an older man."

I really enjoyed that, and took a few seconds to allow the joyful news to sink in. The general all round prospects were looking brighter by the minute. Really cheerful now, I promised that I would call in before week end with my decision. On my way back to Dad's chair, I realised I was grinning my fool's head off. I dropped in to it, very happy. For seconds only, the damned phone jangled yet again. It was Eric, his voice was almost chuckling.

"Would you like to earn a couple of quid?"

"If it's decent, morale, and legal, yes of course."

"Getting choosy now are we? The first two don't usually bother you."

He really was in buoyant mood. "An old school mate of my wife's brought me a hearing aid for repair, but I had some doubts about her paying me. Lady wife assured me she was good, but had married a wrong un. A good worker, but he spent it all on drink. On her say so, I risked it. She promised she would pay me at the beginning of last Month. She's just called to say sorry, they've had a bit of bad luck. Listen to this, it's the best bad luck story ever.

"It appears that her husband left the Black Bull when they chucked him out at three thirty. He drove North on the A60, dropping down the slope towards Mill Lane, he passed a stream of cars. (Thought they were parked) No! they were allowing an old chap on two sticks to cross the road. Hubby's car hit the old chap and knocked him for six. Police and Ambulance arrived, whisked the patient to hospital. Now the real 'bad luck' comes in. He was drunk, no licence or insurance for the car, all four tyres were bald, the brakes were not working, his stop lights did not work, and he had no rear number plate. The pit he works at is miles away, no buses run, no car, no job. But all is saved, He's got a job at the club, emptying beer bottles." At that his control really went for a few minutes. As he recovered he managed to gasp. "The bill is for fourteen pounds, if you get it you can keep four of them."

"Give me the name and address."

"Do you think you can?"

"I can't if I don't try."

He only had her name and the street, no number. No time like the present, I had a quick breakfast and set off.

The street map told me it was a long dead end street, the far side of town. I entered the street on the leg of a 'T', dead end both ways, left and right, all terrace houses. I turned right. Lads playing cricket with a tennis ball and a lamp post for the wicket told me. "It's rate up at yon end youth, but watch ert, there's a woman up theer that's lost 'er cat, she's fair doing 'er nut."

I reversed, drove slowly to the 'other' end. The houses were all in blocks of four, in between each four was a gennel, snicket, passage, entry, whatever district your from. I drove right to the end, pulled up, and got out.

Shock of shocks, a dishevelled 'fussy breeches' appeared out of the last entry. "OOOH Mr Chapman, have you seen my pussy?"

My expression must have been vintage Simon Templar, as I struggled for a suitable reply. Fighting to keep a straight face, I eventually came out with. "Sorry, I've not had the pleasure, is it ginger?"

"Why yes, how on earth did you know?"

Still fighting to keep a straight face, I enquired about the lady I was looking for.

"That's my Auntie, she lives next door. They've had a bit of bad luck and she's had to go to work, what do you want her for?"

I explained that the lady in question owed my friend fourteen pounds, and that I was collecting on his account.

"Wait a minute," and she shot through the front door.

I leaned on the wall with a daft grin on my face, sure, that she had not realised the clanger that she had dropped. When, out of the next entry strolled the largest, most battered, disreputable, ginger tom cat I have ever seen in my life. One ear missing, as was the last few inches of tail. Its face bore the scratches of a recent encounter. I picked it up, no doubt at all, it reeked of 'her' perfume.

She reappeared through the front door, yelped with delight, and took the creature from me, then cooed at it like a mother. "Has my naughty little Tommy been fighting again, you naughty naughty boy." Turning she handed me fourteen pounds. "My Dad has paid it for her, he owns all the houses at this end of the street." All pride. Then with a crafty feline look asked. "Have you got another job yet?"

"Yes, Winston phoned me this morning, he wants me to go back."

The look on her face as I turned to go was worth all the tea in China.

Eric could hardly believe as I handed him a ten pound note, then when I told him who from, we had to share a gleeful grin.

"I wonder if Daddy will ever get his fourteen pounds back?" Eric questioned.

Chapter 19
What Do We Do Now?

Dad walked in with the most silly grin on his face, he had been invited into a cottage further down the street, on the other side. In his jacket pocket, he had the most pretty, appealing little puppy, probably seven or eight weeks old. Mother a nondescript terrier, Father, unknown. It looked like a Manchester Terrier, a black and tan short glossy coat, tiny little teeth like needles, little sticky up ears that curled over on top, bright beady eyes. It took over the household from the word go, apart from me. It 'had' my achilles tendon within minutes. Every visitor suffered, they could stroke it, tickle its tummy till the cow's came home, then just as soon as they turned to go, it turned and nipped. Mum and Dad loved it, everyone else was scared stiff of it.

Dad took it out on Scamp's big old lead that had never been used. It looked ridiculous, that big heavy leather thonged lead on that miniature pup. But none of us dare say so.

Aunt Ethel called, she always tried to time it when Dad was out. Whilst Mum mashed tea, she asked. "Anything happened yet?"

I thanked her for their kind offer, and explained as much as I knew myself. Of course including some of the traumas and upsets, that caused the doubts and fears.

"It's Bob's idea to lend you the money, he holds our purse strings, why don't you come for your tea tonight, then you can thank him yourself. By the way, you have improved the chimney breast.

I was taken aback for a few seconds till I remembered. The very old stone built house plaster was anything but true. Not that it mattered until the sun caught the chimney breast. It looked like a topographical map of the Himalayas. Just before the recent 'upset' Mum wanted to re paper it all, she had asked if I could improve the surface first. I had tried, BUT!

"Bob said there was all credit to you for trying, it's more than your Dad ever does."

Mum arrived with the tea. "He's never ever even offered to knock a nail in for me," she complained.

Dad was about due, Ethel said she must be off, I offered to take her in the car and help prepare tea. As we prepared to go, Mum came out with her classic Autumnal remark, it never ceased to amuse me, Mum never realised why. "My gum, it's getting late early tonight."

Aunt passed the pots out of the cupboard, whilst I put the cloth on and placed pots to instructions. Then I filled the kettle and put it on the fireside trivet, she produced a loaf of bread and a small piece of ham.

"Shall I be cutting the bread?"

"And do me out of my job." Uncle's kind soft voice preceded him through the door. Medium height, of slender build, hair slightly sandy, but going bald, twinkly eyes full of amusement. He took his jacket off, and hung it behind the kitchen door. Removed his bib and brace overalls, and took them out into his shed, back in the kitchen, to meticulously wash his hands. A master joiner by trade. He had made all their furniture, fitted parquet tiles in the room, a real tradesman. Poor Aunt Ethel and Mum could never keep up with his humour. His dry wit and straight face had them both guessing.

I fleetingly remembered him telling Mum during the war. "Had she read that we were taking bombs to Germany?"

That really upset her, she was chuntering away till he said. "They're dropping them."

Ethel was a seamstress, a dressmaker of some skill, she made his shirts, ties etc. she had been small and slim, but in middle age the family 'spread' was beginning to takeover.

Bob was working on a carving knife with the steel. He wielded them with all the skill of a butcher, when satisfied, he began to cut the bread. I was fascinated, I had never ever seen bread cut so thin. That done, he cleaned the knife and started on the ham. I could see the pattern on the plates through all the slices.

Within minutes, I had finished eating, and was still hungry. Four slices of that ham, six slices of bread and butter, had not added to as much as a single slice of each at home. Two halves of a tinned peach with some tinned cream was of little help, nor was a thin wafer of buttered scone. But it was evident that Bob and Ethel were satisfied, they had finished their tea. My stomach was still rumbling its hunger.

With a slow smile of satisfaction, Bob poured us all a further cup of tea, even that was as weak as washing up water. He took one through to the kitchen for his wife, then placed ours, one each side of the fireplace, on the tiles. He motioned me to the far easy chair, whilst settling himself in its sister chair opposite.

Just as soon as he was seated, he asked with his usual

easy smile. "How did you get on plastering the chimney breast?"

With that sort of half smile, I never was sure if another of his 'leg pulls' was due. Not so, he truly was interested. "How much plaster did you drop on the hearth?"

"All on it," I admitted. "I had watched a customer plaster patching, it looked so easy."

"It is when you know how." His smile became even more broad. "How is your swimming now?" The question came as Ethel returned from washing up, both were highly amused.

I am a self taught swimmer, whilst at the junior school, to be one of the 'in' crowd, you had to dive in the River Meraun and swim across what was known locally as 'The Hole'. The river turned a sharp corner, the current over the years had swept away the silt from the corner leaving at least a six foot deep hole. It must have been around ten feet across. I could stand waist deep this side, and the other side, to get across you had to stay afloat. Aged about ten years I had managed it. No breathing, one big deep breath had to do. Arms and legs thrashing like flails I had made it. So full of it I just had to boast to Aunt and Uncle I could swim. So they took me to the town swimming baths to prove the point. "Do you think that you could swim a whole width?"

Keen to prove my point, a huge breath, and off I went, doing my flail act fifteen to the dozen. They picked me from the water at less than half way, gasping for breath, by all accounts I had been stationary for some time. Bursting with laughter they had pointed out that I also needed to breath. Naturally over the years I got to be much better, so much so I felt compelled to tell them of a similar situation during my R.A.F. career.

Whilst on the radio course at Stockport, one Saturday morning the whole Flight was marched to the baths. Five at a time we were lined up at one end and told to swim as fast as possible to the other end. I won. The five winners were lined up, same again, and the next five winners. After winning all, I was told that I was to represent the Flight that afternoon in a swimming gala. Head up and chest out for a few hours till the hour of truth came nigh. The chap in charge announced. The breast stroke event was over FIVE lengths!

I went for it full chat, realised I was not in front as on occasions I saw a flurry of foam ahead. At just over two lengths I was shattered, nothing left at all, I floated, gasping. Then with horror I realised that the event was finished, only me left in the water, the next event was lined up waiting to start.

Slowly, I set off for the side, but the cat calls from my mates had me finishing the full five lengths to a mixture of jeers claps, and yells of encouragement. The most lonely and longest swim of my life.

Both Bob and Ethel were crying as I finished my narrative. With hindsight, I now realise that Bob's were tears of laughter, whilst Ethel's were more with pity for me.

"I reckon a chap who can tell such a story against himself must be alright," eventually came from Bob. "Y'know, your not a bit like your Dad." I glowed at this, it was a real compliment I thought. Bob went on. "Do you remember the one and only time that your Dad attended a family Christmas party?"

Do I ever? Everyone but Dad was laughing about it for days.

Obviously, Dad had told 'them at the pit', that he was going to a party, one chap had suggested the following as a good entertainer.

The 'victim' stood with his head back, a coin on his forehead, a funnel in the top of his trousers. He had to drop the coin off his forehead and catch the coin in the funnel. Dad must catch Bob out on this one.

But Bob was too canny, he just did not understand what Dad meant.

Full of frustration at Bob being so dim, Dad had snatched the funnel and coin from Bob to demonstrate. Quick as a flash Bob had picked up the waiting water jug and emptied the lot. Dad never ever attended another party.

In a more sober fashion now, Bob sort of 'teased' all the latest information from me on the present situation. He then leaned back in his chair, placed the finger tips of both hands together and gave his opinion.

"Well Ron, don't rush into anything, we are not in a position to help you with advice, but if you do decide to have a go we will loan you a thousand pounds, charge you two and a half percent interest. Please pay us back as soon as you can, but please in a lump sum. If you give it us in dribs and drabs, it might not get back in the bank. One further thought. If all these other people want to back you, you must be worth some faith in yourself."

He stood up, and sort of 'shepherded' me towards

the back door, I was almost in tears.

I unlocked the car and slumped in the seat, then the tears really came. Gratitude? Relief? I knew not. Two cigarettes later (Neither Bob or Ethel smoked) I eventually released the handbrake and let the car coast down the hill. Nearing the bottom, I started the engine and engaged second gear and let the clutch out. Nothing happened! The little car just coasted to a standstill. I tried the clutch again, it felt as it should, engaged gear again, nothing!

Switching the engine off, I wound the driver's window down got out, and started to push. Steering through the window it went very well, turned right. still going well, left on to Betts Lane, but when I got to Church Road and the left turn it was a slight up hill. Much harder work, and a good five hundred yards of such to face. I grunted, sweated, strained, realising that if ever I lost momentum, it would be even more difficult. I reached opposite our gate, there had been a stream of traffic both ways, but now a slight lull. I swung the steering over and tried to charge the 'run up' to our gate. No doubt I was tiring, the slight incline was going to beat me. Feet scrabbled for a grip, sweat filled my eyes, I was still failing, then wonder of wonders the car slowly began to move. I had to lean through the window to snatch the handbrake on before it hit the gate. I subsided on the car side, panting, trying to regain my breath. With astonishment I spotted an arthritic, fat, little old lady, dusting her hands before giving me a nod, picking up two heavy looking bags, and limping on her way. "Thank you very much," I sort of wheezed at her. Mum came out of our front door and hobbled towards me.

"What's up lad?" She questioned.

"Dunno, half shaft? crown wheel? pinion? Who was that that gave me a push?

"Mrs. Rambler, you used to sit beside and be sweet on her daughter in your first year in Infants school. Her Audrey was always getting holes in her knickers, so she took a hammer to school to knock a nail down, it was not a nail, the bench seat had splinters."

I was trying to amass this information as I opened, and fastened the gate back. The things you learn when you get older. "What was this Audrey like then?"

"Chocolate box pretty, with long blonde hair."

"Where is she now then?"

"I'm not sure, they went to live at Newark, the last rumour I heard was that Audrey was in a loony bin."

Shaking my head at the puzzle of all this, breathing now back to normal, Mum trying to help, we pushed the car into the Garage.

The following morning, I rolled the car out on to the grass, put my screw Jack under the centre of the differential housing, lifted the car, and took both back wheels off. Un noticed, the edge of the jack base dug into the soft ground. With a muffled sort of 'crunch', the jack tipped and the car subsided on to its brake drums. I sat back on my heels, horror stricken. The number of times at the Garage when we had all preyed for someone to invent 'sky hooks'. I really needed such now. Lifting gear no good, no where to put it, Jack no good, too low to get one under, four strong blokes might do the trick, but where do I find four strong young men? I really need a buxom bare breasted blonde to stand by the gate as bait. I don't know one that would.

Dad appeared out of the back door, full of 'purpose' he walked towards me. "What the bleddy hell 'ave yer dun ner? I thought you were supposed to know all abert cars?"

I began to try and explain, but was cut off short.

"A bloody fool on 'ossback would 'ave known what would 'appen. Get yoursen ready wi' your jack and some wood, I'll pick it up."

"You can't."

"Course I bloody can."

He stood, impatient, while I scuttled to the shed to find a piece of old plank. I got under as far as I could, wood ready, other hand to gather the jack. He bent, took hold of the bumper bar, and picked the whole thing up, just like that! Wood and jack in place, it teetered, just on balance. "Get yoursen some bricks under the sides to hold it's balance." He instructed, his 'lift' seemed effortless. At high speed, behind the shed this time I found a half dozen bricks. Three under each running board were just right.

Dad just dusted his hands, and 'chuntered' his way back to the house. "Yer should 'ave got yersen a proper job dern t' pit, then yer'd 'ave known."

I stayed on my knees, still with heavy breathing, wondering about it all. Then realised, when they delivered his ton of coal each month, he'd got the lot into the coal house in under twenty minutes. He could have three shovel fulls in midair before the first one landed. He had only once ever called me Ron. "Ee, 'Im, or 'are

185

youth'." I mentally went through the situations. "Is ee in? Ave yer sin im?" It was when he had blood clots on the brain, I had followed the ambulance to Sheffield Royal Hospital. The specialist spoke in a broad Yorksire accent. "I reckon it's blood clots, goo an' get yoursen a bite of lunch while I drill a few holes in his head to find out."

Naturally I had not eaten, I had wandered round Sheffield in a daze, returned to find Dad, still out, head swathed in bandages, hands covered in huge cotton wool gloves. They explained, that was to stop him tearing at his bandaged head. The specialist called by to say. "I were right, I found three clots, yer can sit wee 'im till ee comes round." Dad's eyes were sunk in deep holes, the holes full of liquid. I queried with a nurse. She explained as she bathed the liquid away. "It's only sweat, a reaction to the drugs we've given him."

Mr Hardman's head appeared round the ward door. "By the way, he's not allergic to iodine and penicillin is he?"

"Yes, both."

"Bloody 'ard lines then. he's pumped full of, and lathered with one or the other."

Dad opened both his eyes. "Ron, what are you doin' ere?" Then passed out again. That was the one and only time I ever heard him call me by name.

After all he had suffered, broken back, crushed foot, all arms and legs broken, blood clots, a piece of steel that wandered around inside his body at will. They never did know if it was from a pit accident or shrapnel from the war. In spite of it all, he had picked up my car like a piece of thistledown. To cap it all, I realised that he never

186

ever would forgive me for not 'werking darn t' pit'.

The mind kept wandering. When Dad was off work so many months with his crushed foot. It had gone gangrene so often it was feared that he would lose it. When eventually the healing process began, he had sat in his 'pit' chair by the bottom 'clothes post', with his leg up on the always present beer box. (Mother used it to hang out washing) One of the real old colliers had called to see him. He had brought Dad an ounce of 'Erinmore' tobacco and as always his faithful Staffordshire Bull Terrier. All that nice mown grass was too much of a temptation to the dog. He 'squatted' and did a pile. The nasty, bad tempered old lady property owner from next door came screaming out of her back door.

"Dirty filthy bloody colliers, and their even worse dogs fouling 'her' grass."

Owd Bob had not turned a hair. "Dunna fesh yoursen missis, if wiv brought owt yer dinna want we'll tek it back we us." He just picked up. (The thankfully dry terds) And dropped them in his pocket.

After 'Owd Bob' had gone, Dad told me about the time when Bob had been almost scalped under a fall of stone. Dr. Court had lifted the flap of flesh, cleaned it with carbolic and stitched it back. He returned in a few days and was surprised that the wound showed no signs of healing. He was some time getting at the truth. It appeared that Bob had still gone to work regularly. After every shift, his wife had snipped the stitches, washed out with carbolic, and restitched the wound.

"That's weer yer find real men, darn t' pit." Dad had explained to his terrified off spring. I realised yet again, I was not built of that sort of material.

With a sigh, I withdrew the near side drive shaft, it had twisted and sheared like a carrot, leaving at least two inches of shaft in the diff. unit. I withdrew the other side, also showing signs of 'twist'. An old Ford ten brake rod out of the shed pushed the bit out and through. With a wry grin at Dad's regular comments. "What der yer keep all this bloody rubbish for?"

First thing in the morning, a worker's return bus ticket into town. (Eight old pence) to the nearest Morris agent. The store keeper greeted me like a long lost brother. We had not seen each other since before I joined up. Frank's hair was now grey, he had also 'developed' a grey beard, he looked like Father time. He still wore the same blue tinted spectacles, his attitude towards customers had not changed a jot.

My request for a half shaft for a 1928 Morris Eight was met by a hoot of derision. "Yer'll not get one from anywhere youth, snap like carrots they do. Ner if yer can fit a pair of thirty seven 'ten' shafts, they'll last fer ever."

"I just need the one for now," I explained.

"To you my friend, anything but, they are bought in pairs, they are sold in pairs, in any case the 'other' side will go any minute I can assure you. You either take my last pair of 'ten' shafts or scrap your motor."

Speech finished, he turned on his heels and disappeared amongst his rows of racking. Back he came with a pair of rusty shafts, the splines protected with sticky tape, the pair fastened together with more of the same.

"Will they fit, and how much are they?"

Eyes gleaming behind his blue specs Frank perused his huge list of prices. He looked up with a broad grin. "I know they can be fitted by a good mechanic, if you're good enough I do not know. I have supplied too many to not know. I am a good store keeper, a poor mechanic. The choice is yours, this is my last pair. The price should be Five pounds nineteen and eleven pence each, to you my friend because I have known you for years, the price is ten pounds the pair." The blue eyes still gleamed, the grin was glued to his face.

"I don't think I have," I started.

"What I will do is let you take them after taking your all from your pocket. Tomorrow I want either the shafts back or the balance. This is 'special' to you my friend, because I have known you for so many years." He passed the shafts over the counter. I emptied my wallet, four pounds only. That disappeared magically, he waited. I dug in my trouser pocket, a few oddments of change only. "Keep that, you will need your bus fare, we close at six p.m. tomorrow."

So we parted, Frank with four pounds and an I.O.U. in his till, me down to coppers.

He was right, the splines did fit, but the shafts were too long, I had to take the knave plates off the wheels to allow about an inch of protrusion each side. Mum loaned me the last six pounds of her 'washing money' kitty. She took in washing to help the family budget, her top charge was sixpence for a full family wash and she used her own soap. It was all in coppers, three penny bits, and the odd sixpence. Dad did have a bundle of notes in his tin at the top of the cupboard, but no one ever dare touch it or ask.

Back at the Morris agents, Frank looked aghast at the pile of small change. "Have you been charging for your services?" he questioned.

I explained at least some of my predicament, he looked at me long and hard. Then pushed the pile of small change back, instructed. "Settle when your ship comes in," with a grin and a wink he screwed my I.O.U. up in a ball and tossed it in to the bin. I had tears pricking the back of my eyes all the way home.

Chapter 20
It Is Time To Decide

I had only been out of bed minutes when an urgent rapping at the front door had me scurrying towards it. A radiant Clare began to gabble at me.

"It's smashing Ron, I really do like it, I just knew that I could trust you to find me just what I wanted." Then taking my face in her two hands she kissed me full on the mouth. Then I realised that Mum was by my side almost looking as flabbergasted as I. Clare gabbled again. "How much do I owe you, I knew I could trust your lad." Mum just looked on in surprise.

"This is Edna's sister," I started to explain.

"Well invite her in, give her a cup of tea, remember your manners."

Clare was in full flow again. "Your lad is real clever," as she stepped inside. "I just knew he would know what I wanted." Mum glowed as I fled to the kitchen to fill the kettle.

Whilst it was doing its best on the fastest of the only two gas jets that worked, I opened my wallet to find her furniture invoice. How much should I put on?" I decided on twenty percent and worked out the answer on the back of the flimsy copy. Doing my best to look and feel nonchalant, I left the kettle to its own devices and sauntered back up the passage, told Clare my answer.

"Ooooh smashing luv, I thought it would be much more than that." She opened her purse, produced it all plus ten shillings, and handed it over. "Now I need some kitchen floor covering, again, I leave it with you."

I looked at Mum for help, no way, she just admitted that she used pegged rugs.

The look on Clare's face put that idea in its place. I had to laugh as thoughts took over, they both waited.

"Last year I had this problem, she liked the carpet so much she covered it with Co Co matt to protect it, then to protect that she put newspaper down. Fresh newspaper every day till visitors came, then off with all to reveal the original. The last I heard she had washed some potato sacks to use instead."

"I'm not like that," Clare assured.

"So please help, just give me a hint," I pleaded.

"No duck, I still leave it with you," another kiss full on the mouth and she was gone.

"What a nice lady," from a glowing Mum.

In funds again, I went into town to pay Frank. He refused, all he had to say was. "Your ship is not even in harbour yet, you will need that and more ere long, see me when your out of the wood."

Blinking like mad I went over to the shop. Talk about the return of the prodigal, Churchill was all over me. He offered either a fixed wage, or a better wage plus commission, or the same wage plus more commission.

Any doubts I may have had, this settled them. I thanked him, explained I now had 'other' irons in the fire, and set off towards home. On route I had second thoughts and stopped in the same woods that I had parked during the 'hole in the foot' episode. I was parked in almost the identical spot, lit a cigarette and pondered. "I wonder why I have never heard from her?"

Then thought of the last time I had seen her. I had

called 'on spec', she had just finished bathing and was wearing only a dressing gown. I had never 'had any' nude before, too good a chance to miss. In no time at all, everything was off apart from my socks. It was all very pleasant, till we heard the back door open. Before big sister could open the inner door I was through the stairs door and shivering. I tried to dress, but scared of making some noise I just shivered. Big sister seemed to stay for ages, talking about nothing at all. I assumed?? that Linda had managed to get her dressing gown on again, I never had found out, by the time the lady went we felt too chastened and lucky to continue any activities.

Mum spoke just as soon as I got in.

"You've had a phone call, Bert has invited you to a party to wet the baby's head, you won't get drunk will you?"

"What did you tell him?"

"That you would go of course." Grunting with pain she waddled her way back to the kitchen.

With miserable thoughts, I flopped into Dad's chair. Bert could not afford to be throwing parties, and my own situation would not allow me to help. The phone rang, it was Eric. "We are going to Bert's tonight, my car's not well, can you pick me up?"

"I don't think we should go, Bert can't afford parties."

"He can, Mog is helping with his brewery allowance, they were fixing it the night of my do at the Hare."

"He can't."

"He already has, you know Mog, it will all be well and truly organised. Have you bought the baby a present?" Silence! "I thought not, meet me outside Eales shop just before five thirty."

Both in our best suits, I eventually settled on a silver tea spoon, with Eric laughing fit to burst.

"What's so funny?"

"Your fame is already spreading, he gave you ten percent discount and I did not even have to ask." I just looked puzzled. "You'll learn as time goes on," he promised, his grin would have done any Cheshire cat proud.

Dad was out with the dog, so Mum made us both a cup of tea whilst we wasted some time. She insisted that we should not arrive early. Still very worried, she 'quizzed' Eric on all possible pitfalls. He was as honest as he could be, without giving her cause for concern. She mentioned that a delighted Clare had called and paid, that reminded me to pay up on our bet. That caused more worry in case her lad had turned into a 'betting man'. Eric as usual smoothed it all by saying it was just a bit of fun on his instigation.

Then Eric said that he had called to see Widow Wells, who would be very pleased to rent me a bedroom for five shillings a week. "Please call and see her soon," he advised.

There must have been about twenty people milling around in Bert's house by the time we arrived. Before we could be introduced to anyone, Mog also arrived. We were led, a bewildered trio, to nod at and shake hands with a blur of different faces. Last in line, Mae brought her school friend, Alice. Well over a stone heavier than Mae, but it was all in the right places. Very mature for her age, a cupid's bow mouth, lathered in lipstick, a plumpish pretty face, dumpling's well and truly 'boiling over'.

"So this is Uncle Ron then?" Sizing all my statistics up with one glance.

"It is," from Mae as she melted herself into my arms for a big 'hello' kiss.

"My turn now," Alice almost engulfed me, I was glad to come up for air. Mae was looking rather peeved, Alice very chuff.

Mog muttered in my ear. "Grab that now youth, before it gets over ripe."

A grinning Bert arrived with three bottles of M. & B. "Yer don't need glasses due yer?"

Then Mae presented the pale weird one, first seen at the 'Hare'. Name Horace (he did look like a Horace) his Daddy was in the Motor Trade. Mae was on my knee, She could not fail to hear Mog's comment. "He still looks as though he's spent the last few months under a bucket with the rhubarb." Her bottom wriggled on my knee as she giggled, quite pleasant really.

As the drink flowed, our trio began to feel more at ease. Clare managed to get me from under Mae to thank me again for her kitchen suite, then began to tell all and sundry how clever I was. I motioned her to be quiet, she asked why, so I took her into the kitchen to explain that it was all still very underhand till everything was properly 'sorted'. Alice was in there, dispensing drinks for all and sundry, and pushed past us with a loaded tray. When she returned, Clare and I were in a huddle whilst I was trying to explain to her the full situation. Quite in a huff, she stormed out again looking very displeased.

"I wish I had some of what you've obviously got." Clare commented. I looked blank, she went back to the front room even more amused than ever.

Back in the room, Eric and Mog were settled at each end of the settee, so I plonked myself between them. Nearly everyone else was gathered around listening to Eric. This yarn was about a relative of his named Graham. He also had started as a mechanic, but fed up with the measly wage he had gone lorry driving. He was a hard worker, and within weeks was promoted to drive the 'Wood drug'. Must explain at this point, in those days, tree's were felled in the forest, branches lopped off, and the whole trunk was transported back to the wood yard. A small compact cab, with a big engine towed two separate axles joined by a long girder. We are talking sixty feet long at least. With such an outfit, four or five tree trunks could be transported at once. Graham was driving North, empty, to fetch more trees from North of the County. A small Ford tried to overtake. He got past the rear axle, but before he could totally overtake, they met a large convoy of army lorries. Spaced with the regulation forty feet between each, the poor little Ford travelled for miles, trapped between Graham's front and rear wheel axles.

None of us had realised, but not one was by now 'feeling any pain', the bladder's were under pressure, only one toilet, but clever Mog had bought bottles of Whisky, a blend none of us had tried. Black bottle, very smooth, not at all harsh, and very 'more' ish, we all approved his choice. The glasses were handed to Alice, she filled and returned them, a good time was being had by all. Around midnight, Eric confided in a whisper to me. "This Black Bottle must be good, I reckon I can take my whisky, but I don't feel at all well." With that, he bolted for the loo... Mog, Bert, and I followed, full of concern. We stood outside like lemons, listening to the most awful retching sounds from within, then, silence!

Bert was the first to move, the door was not bolted, but he could not force it open. Mog, the slimmest by far, managed to get one eye round the door. "He's passed out in front of the bowl," he announced. "All curled up in a ball." Now Mog had a war time medal for forcing his way into a bomb bay full of primed bombs. They had been released, but the bomb bay doors had not opened, they all lay, primed, on the closed bomb doors. He insists that he was not brave, but the only armourer on the squadron thin enough to get through the gap. We voted him for the job.

He sort of 'wriggled his way in'. "Out like a light," he announced. Then pointed out that he would stand on the seat, pick Eric upright, so that we could open the door. Much grunting and heaving was heard before we got the door open.

Between us, we half carried, half dragged him through to the settee. He looked ghastly, a sort of yellowy green. Edna produced spare rugs to cover him. Sobered by now, people were beginning to go, some others took the hint. Bert and Edna were in serious earnest conversation with Mother of Alice. Then Edna sloped off to make a mass of strong black coffee, whilst Bert announced their deliberations. Eric was to stay on the settee. Mog would sleep in Mae's bed, whilst I was to be 'put up' by Mum of Alice, in the bed of Alice, whilst Mae and Alice slept in the three quarter bed recently vacated by the now married big sister.

Bert came out of the kitchen brandishing an almost empty bottle of Vodka. "Whose bin on Vodka?" We all looked blank till Mog chipped in.

"I don't drink the stuff, it was in my first allocation, still sealed, so I thought I might as well bring it, just in case." The latter in an apologetic tone.

Bert looked round, almost angry, and spotted a guilty looking Alice. "Do you know what we ought to know?"

"Well, er, the whisky was going so fast, your on the last bottle, so I've been putting Vodka in before filling up with whisky. I've not done anything wrong have I?" Her big goo goo eyes so full of innocence.

"I will sort her out in the morning, now is not the time," from her irate Father.

All hilarity gone, we had all sobered magically. Then realised it would not be sense for anyone to drive home. The eventual decision was to let sleeping dogs lie rather than disturb any one at home at this late hour. I gave a huge sigh of relief, imagining Dad's temper at being woken this late.

We all had yet another black strong, coffee, mine tasted really bitter, then I was 'collected' by Alice and Mae to take me to bed. When I got outside in the cool air, I almost 'went'. But support from the two girls had me almost under control. Their arms round me, my arms around each of them. Alice moved my hand so that it rested on her ample bosom, so I also moved my other hand on to Mae's smaller, firmer, model. "What a pleasant way to be taken to bed," my bemused thoughts decided.

The girls were dispatched to bed, I was almost 'force fed' another black coffee and a sandwich by Mum of Alice. Dad of Alice took me upstairs, showed me the whereabouts of the essential rooms, before steering me to the boudoir of Alice. No doubts at all, very feminine, all sort of lacy and filmy, it even sort of smelled of Alice. Unlike 'Fussy Breeches', this was quite nice. I peed, washed, put my suit on a hanger behind the door, and sat on the bed in my underpants, wondering how I ought to dress for bed.

A tap on the door, in walked Alice, her nightie was not really a 'see through', but it left nothing to the imagination.

"Scuse me Uncle Ron, I need my dressing gown." She was heading across to the wardrobe. I sat with my hands over my 'essentials' wondering. She changed direction, came towards me, saying, "That IS a nice hairy chest, and put her hand out to stroke it.

"Good night Alice," I said in what I hoped was a very firm voice.

Another gentle knock and in came Mae. "I thought I might find you here, Come to bed this instant." Pausing only to give me yet another good night kiss she shepherded an unwilling Alice from the room. I waited a while, then got up to look in the wardrobe, there was a very flimsy dressing gown, right in front. "What to do?" To deliver it was putting my head in the lion's mouth, to leave it, was to say the least, risky. I returned to the edge of the bed to sit and think some more. I was cold, thought "Aw bugger it," stripped off my pants, put them under the pillow, and slipped between the sheets. The day, the drink, soon had me in the land of nod.

I don't know the time, or how long I had been asleep, when I became wide awake. It was still dark, I had a head full of hammers, was bursting for a pee, and had a huge hard on.

With sigh of resignation, I put my underpants on and found the toilet. No way could I force 'it' down to the bowl. It was well and truly erect. As it was I would have sprayed the ceiling, but when I forced it down I could do nothing. Then I knelt and rested it on the cold porcelain, that did cool it's ardour enough to allow relief. Next dilemma, do I flush and risk disturbing some one, or be unclean and leave it. I flushed and nipped back to my room. Within minutes I was fast asleep again.

My next impression was yet another massive 'hard on', I tried to hold it with my hands, but I could not move them, they were both above my head. Then something like cool hands were ministering to it, before it was immersed in something warm and wet. Within seconds I ejaculated, panic stricken I tried to find my handkerchief, my hands still would not move. In panic now, I became wide awake, switched the light on and desperately looked for the tell tale 'stain'. Not a sign, with a silly rueful smile I realised that it must have been a very realistic dream.

Whatever was left of the night, I 'catnapped', till sounds of activity below had my eyes creaking open, with a slam, they shut again. The daylight was blinding. I had to gently squeak them open till they got used to it.

Then with a head that weighed a ton I dressed and shambled to the toilet. Used it and the wash bowl with what energy I could muster and returned to my bedroom, on a sudden whim, I opened the wardrobe door, not a sign of the dressing gown? Deep in thought, unshaven, I put on my tie and jacket and almost staggered downstairs. Not looking or feeling anything like my best.

Mum of Alice greeted me with a cheerful. "Good morning Ron, had a good night? It's a dull old morning."

"Er um yes, I thought it was too bright. But I had some frightening dreams."

"Breakfast? Egg bacon, sausage, tomato, fried bread?"

Any other day I would have said a big yes please, it sounded superb, but my stomach revolted.

"Just toast and gallons of tea if you please."

I sort of 'flopped' on the kitchen chair she had pulled out for me.

"You do look a bit delicate," she smiled to soften the comment. "My Bill has gone to give Bert a hand to clear up, the girls are still in bed. Alice will get a telling off when Bill gets back."

"But if she did not know any better."

"She'll still have sore ears," but the smile did not sound quite as threatening.

"Has she got a sister?"

"Why yes, but she's married and away now, I did not have half the problems and worry with her that I do with Miss Hotpants upstairs. I will sigh with relief when she is married and off my hands."

I clambered to my feet, thanking her for all that she

had done, and saying that it would be sense to get back to Bert's and look at Eric."

The walk back seemed much longer than it was last night, a good thing, as by the time I got back to number eighty eight I was almost human.

A ghastly looking Eric sat staring at a mug of black coffee, the coffee stared back at him, showing no signs of pity. "Do you think you will live?" I asked in what I hoped was a jocular fashion.

"I look and feel like death warmed up," he decided. I could not vouch for how he felt, but he was right about how he looked.

Bert was busy filling me in. "Glad I'm a beer man and keep off spirits, he looked terrific. Mog has rushed back to the West Midlands, Bill gave us a hand here before going to the shop. Edna began to berate all and sundry for our lack of sense, Bert was looking sheepish before a sound from upstairs had him rushing. Back he came with the 'little bundle', with great pride and care he uncovered the little face. It looked to me like an old wizened orange. But Bert was full of him. "He was asleep last night, we would not disturb him. A right little smasher in't ee?"

Edna poured even more black coffee into Eric and I. (It was many years before I could ever face black coffee again.) I drove a feeble Eric home and dropped him off, went home myself, and drove into the yard. Before I could get out of the car, our back door slammed and out came an annoyed Dad at full speed.

"Stop theer and listen," he instructed. "Another trick like that an' your ert on yer ear, while you live 'eer, you live by our rules. If ever there's a next time, all yer clothes will be in a pile on t' yard."

"But Dad, I'm nearly thirty."

"I done care if you're bloody ninety, just remember what I'm saying." He charged back indoors and slammed the door behind him.

Within a few seconds, with a furtive glance behind, Mum arrived.

"What happened lad? We were worried sick."

I explained about a young lady mixing drinks without knowing better, we all thought it sense to not drive, she chipped in.

"You could have phoned."

"And wake Dad up after midnight?" She nodded in understanding.

Chapter 21
All Worry Gone? Ha Ha

Edna's sister had bought a kitchen carpet, the lady across the road had a kitchen suite, two more friends of friends had bought room carpets, all cash sales, all was looking rosy. Then I remembered I had not as yet been to see Widow Wells. She really was a sweet little old lady, almost bent double with arthritis, her face really creased with 'pain' lines. It was all a struggle for her on her small pension. Six of her seven sons were married and away, the youngest lived away, but returned when he was out of money due to his gambling and drinking, he sounded to be a real 'neer do well'. I gave her two pounds for the next four weeks rent, she was all but in tears. Embarrassed, I turned to go, but she stopped me.

"Did I know how to fill in a football coupon?" I nodded. Would I please fill one in for her. Another nod. She produced a well folded entry coupon from her 'pinny' pocket and handed it over. It was for this week. I decided on the numbers by asking questions, she had seven sons, she had been one of nine brothers and sisters, her house number was Thirty nine, her birthday was on the twenty first, so we soon had eight numbers. She was so pleased, handed over her sixpence, and would I post it? I had not the heart to mention the cost of postal order and stamp, but posted it that very day.

I went to a local factory, bought a dozen cardboard 'chicken' boxes, they had 'finger' or air holes at each end, all of a size to take such as shirts, cardigans, jumpers, etc folded neatly. All fitted in the car, so I bought twelve more and took them round to Widow Wells the next week. She was most effusive, her thanks were embarrassing, that one line on the treble chance had won her just over a thousand pounds. She shook my hand warmly and said she would not embarrass me by offering any, as any time I was short I was clever enough to do myself a line and win again. 'On such, faith in a person is built.' I consoled myself.

The bank manager insisted I should employ a solicitor, and I must form a limited company. No cash would be forthcoming, as Uncle Bob would stand surety for a thousand pounds.

Not very happy about this, I went to ask Uncle Bob.

"No way," he was emphatic. I have known a lot of people become guarantors, they have lost all. I will, as promised, lend YOU a thousand pounds. I suggest that you use another bank." So I did.

Panic over? Not really. When Bob went for the money, he was told it was in a ninety day account, if he withdrew now he would lose interest. So we had to wait. I had told Bill and Ben I would not need their money, BUT! in the interim they agreed I could sell 'their' electrical goods, for them, using THEIR credit terms and charges, which I would collect FOR them. Of course it meant a lot more 'booking' for me, and more 'profit' for them, but beggars are not in a position to choose.

I did not approach any of Solomon's customers, but hardly a day went by without a message arriving by some means or other, asking me to call. Some of course were not in a position to 'pay them up', so, I had to wait a few weeks for them. One pair in this predicament were Bert and Edna. Naturally I did call and see them when in the area. Nearly slipped up one night, Supervisor John was still doing the round, and had almost turned it right round. He had only just gone when I called. Bert was giggling quietly. John had been really pleading for an order as he was losing customers hand over fist. John asked, "If ever they saw me would they please plead with me to go back, they had not found anyone so good."

I told him we didn't see owt on yer.

The following day, on a sudden whim I drove past Linda's old house. It looked desolate, empty and deserted. The bare upstairs windows looked 'unseeing' across the street. Down stairs was out of sight down the slope. I was driving slowly, looking, thinking. So engrossed I almost knocked over a young lady scuttling across the street in front of the car. Panic brake, followed by dropping a window to apologise. "So sorry," I started.

"No matter, it's you I want anyway. I've had a letter from the Mrs, for you, ages. She's sent you a postal order. Can't think why she sent it to me, I'm new on the street. I would have thought it better to Mrs. Radford, I know she did trade with you. Please wait a moment." She turned and went round the back of her house. A very young delectable body. Good boobs, tiny trim waist, long long legs, short skirt, no underskirt, and a little pretty bum that looked like it had been stuck on as an after thought.

"I bet her inside leg is at least thirty three inch," I drooled as she wriggled it all round the house end.

I knew why Linda had not approached Mrs. Radford. A large, ungainly ugly masculine woman. She had sneered at me for ages.

"You're spending some time across the road, are you signing her rent book for her? I don't think you have ever called when the husband is in." All accompanied by a very lewd grin.

After that I always parked outside Mrs. Radford's house and walked across and down the few yards. No more such comments.

Almost before I had finished my reverie, the young body appeared again out of her front door, brandishing the flimsy postal order. "I thought it might be better to catch you, rather than give it to Mrs. Radford?"

I nodded, in appreciation at her astuteness from one so young.

As she handed the order to me, I was surprised to see a wedding ring on her finger. "You look very, very young to be married." I felt forced to comment.

"I am, but I played with fire and got burned." She admitted with a pretty little hint of a blush. "We got married just as soon as we were sure, before the signs show. They'll still talk of course, but they won't be so sure."

All this came out of a pretty, frank, open face. I appreciated what I saw and heard. I unfolded the postal order, it was for a little more than Linda's bill, but still amounted to only shillings.

"No letter or message with it?" I asked, hoping. She shook her head.

"Do you know where she is?" The head shook yet again.

"If you do start on your own please give me a call." Then she turned and wriggled it all back through her front door. I just sat and stared with surprise for some minutes.

Imagine the word "how" was beginning to form on my lips.

I had met Dot England in the street, she had ordered a mass of bedding from me and paid cash. We spent a tearful half hour saying "sorry" to each other, and pleading. "Could we please still be good friends."

By the time the solicitor had all the paper work prepared, Bill & Ben had printed me a sort of pass book on firm green card. It folded into three, a different appearance, size, and shape to any other credit drapers around.

The following Friday night, it had been good business. The little car was speeding home in a sort of darkish twilight. It bustled through a twisty bit in a small spinney. "Something?" in the middle of the road. I covered the brake pedal and flicked the lights from 'dip' to 'main beam'. A female body sprawled in the centre, skirt hiked up to reveal some panty, head on one arm. I pulled up right in front to protect the body from other traffic and left all the lights on. But! as I reached for the door catch, out of the corner of my eye I spotted a large unkempt looking character sprinting from the cover of the trees, AND, the body was getting to its feet! I delayed opening the car door for a few seconds, then when he reached for the handle to drag it open, I flung it open with all the strength I could muster. "Whooosh", all the air went out of him, and he dropped as though pole axed. The girl was now fast approaching my door. I put one leg out, stood on it, and met her full in the face with my flat hand over the bonnet, I distinctly heard and felt cartilage 'scrunch'. Back in the car, I reversed just enough to miss the two bodies, and drove off as fast as the car would go.

I screeched to a standstill at the Police Station in the next village, rushed inside trembling like a leaf to report on the situation. The portly, kindly, almost ready for retirement duty Sergeant sat me down, supplied tea and a cigarette before listening to my gabble. Then before he started form filling asked, was I a collector and was this my usual time.

I thought, then realised, yes, I had been around this time for months.

"Have none of you the sense you were born with?" he asked. "You do the same route and time week after week, then wonder why the hijacker has you sussed. I suppose you keep it all in one wallet or bag?"

I had to nod, ashamed at the obvious.

"This is the third within months, the others lost all, I hope you have given them both a headache they won't forget in a hurry. He took all my details, looked at my licence, then filled in a statement for me to sign.

"You say you hit him with the car door, is it damaged? If it is I will also need an accident report filled in."

I had to admit I was so panic stricken I had never thought.

"Let's go and look," he grinned and picked up a lantern almost the size of a search light. Poor door, a huge dent covered it all. He, with great deliberation, opened and closed the door a few times, then mused.

"Good these coach built doors, you would never

have got a new one to close after a belt like that. These wooden frames are really strong, I've read somewhere that they were made of hardwood. Let's get the report done then you can clear off home.

A sad thoughtful man drove off slowly. Poor little car door, what do I say to my parents? Mum would worry herself sick, Dad would look on me as hopeless for not dusting them both up and handing them in. I decided that a gust of wind had snatched it from my hand against a lamppost. No, a telegraph pole would be best as a lamp post would be painted.

In the morning I fetched the retired old 'body man' from the garage, just to look? Not looking as young as he did, I then realised that he must have been retired for more than ten years. He did the usual tooth sucking 'it will never ever be the same again' routine, but could not hide his delight at being able to use his skills again. Within minutes, he had the door off, wound the window down and set off home with it over his shoulder.

I sat on the running board and debated, I could not use it without a door, leaving it for ten minutes and it would be very empty on my return, not as yet any big outstanding accounts, all of them were safe anyway. The little bus had been streaming smoke of late. Almost on impulse, I got the starting handle out to feel the compressions. Not really any. That decided me. I phoned Eric's wife with instructions. Turned the car around, backed it into the garage, ran the front wheels on to three bricks each side, then went in to find my very oldest old clothes. Looking like a tramp that has hit bad times I started. Sump drained, radiator drained, Cylinder head off. It was much worse than I thought.

Loads of 'slop' on every piston, three exhaust valves burnt out, the fourth looking very ill.

I was just about to 'drop' the third connecting rod when Eric arrived.

He picked up one of the rods, looking at the big ends before he spoke.

"You said nowt about bearings, these have shot it. Morris only do a five thou. oversize piston, Wellworthy do a long skirt piston with an extra ring below the gudgeon pin. They do them in five thou. stages from five to thirty oversize, can't get any until tomorrow, you will need valves as well, and we shall have to borrow two micrometers to see what we can get away with."

I crawled from under looking very worried.

He cracked out laughing. "You're as dirty and unkempt as a chap I used to know at the garage."

I looked through the driver's wing mirror. Filthy, oil and dirt on my face, in my hair. Old shirt lathered in black oil stains. I looked and felt pig sick.

Eric was scowling, looked first at the piston and rod in his hand, then felt for 'slop' on the piston still in situ, his little finger explored the 'seat' of a valve in the open position, then made his laconic announcement. "Cut yer losses and get rid."

"Don't be bloody silly, I can't."

"Don't you be bloody silly, you've got to."

"Who would buy this? Especially in bits, if I reassemble it, the carbon seal has gone, it probably won't even start."

I went quiet, I could see he was deep in thought.

Then he decided. "Get them valves out as soon as you've dropped the last rod, start decoking, I will see what I can find." He put everything he thought he might need in a cardboard box and left me to it.

I decoked everything, the four passable inlet valves, valve ports, head, really intended to do a bodge job, but training won. The engine block was washed in paraffin, all carbon removed with screwdriver, wire brush, emery cloth. When I had to finish because of lack of light it all still gleamed, even as night was setting in. I was surprised how late it was. Good old Mum had put a large saucepan of water on the fire, so I did manage a good wash and supper before 'hitting the sack'. No news or sign of Eric.

I was even awake before Dad left for work (unheard of). Just as soon as I heard the gate shut I was out and had started valve grinding. Mum called me in for tea and a sort of breakfast after I had good seats on the four inlet valves. Out to the yard again, to clean and reset the plugs, and points when I heard the gate squeak. I looked up in anticipation. The body man, complete with my door, a complacent look on his gnarled old face. "I did tell you that it would never be the same?" he questioned. My heart began to sink as he sort of 'twirled' my door off his shoulder for inspection. Relief, the smooth sand papered mixture of filler, undercoat, paint and gleaming steel, looked perfect to me. I commented so.

"Not when it gets a coat of gloss it not. It's good paint, what did you use?"

"Valspar."

"I thought as much, it's hardly 'spelched' at all. Have

you got any left?"

With a grin of satisfaction I sped to the shed, returning in minutes with a half tin, lid hammered down, and sealed with masking tape. He held it to his ear and rocked the tin. We were both happy to hear the 'slopping' sound that ensued. "Who told you how to look after paint?" he questioned.

"Just part of my general garage education I guess."

Nodding at my dismembered car, he carried on. "It looks as though you've enough on your plate, I'll finish what I've started, I've brought my own dove grey undercoat. Weer can I 'ang it?"

I nodded to a solid roof beam above our heads.

"Gorranywire?"

I went to the shed and produced a roll of fencing wire. He dropped a large back pack off his other shoulder and delved within. What an assortment. Brushes, sheets of emery cloth, blocks, thinners, and primer paint. Standing on the old faithful beer crate, he hung the door on the wire to his required height, then sat on the beer crate, looked at the door, and lit a cigarette, deep in thought. Said "Just the job," stubbed out his cigarette, and started work.

We worked on without another word passing between us till Eric arrived, complete with a brand new set of standard big end shells. "Can you afford these if they fit?" He really was gloating.

"Why, how much?" The worry starting up again.

"Five bob from that little garage in Putney, he asked for two pounds ten, but I pointed out it could well be his last chance to get rid, I had to barter a lot, an' if they're no good, you still owe me five bob. Here's an outside mic., dive under and let's know the worst."

I was under in no time at all, beads of worry on my brow. In luck, hardly more than a trace of 'ovality'. I thanked my lucky stars I had always used good engine oil and always changed it well before the advised time. Grinning, I emerged from under and gave my opinion.

All I got from Eric was "Jammy bugger."

"What about pistons valves, etc.?

With a warning glance at the body man he just said. "I need to negotiate with the boss man, he was not in today."

"How will that do you both then?" The body man with a note of pride in his voice. The door was swinging on its wire support, it gleamed, pristine was the first impression, not a brush mark to be seen. Then as it swung in the light, a very slight indentation showed. "Sorry, I did say I could not get it perfect," the man apologised.

"How on earth to get a finish like that with a brush?" Eric had to ask.

"Ovver fifty five years' practice," he grinned as he began to pack his bag. "Don't try to 'ang it back on the car for at least thirty six hours," he warned.

"What do I owe you?" I blurted.

"Nowt, you've both done me lots of favours over the years, just let me 'ave a couple of quid when yer boat comes in." His old face split into a grin as he hoisted his bag on his back and set off for the gate.

Looking back, I now realise how lucky and well I had done. With the help of Eric and the body man all was ship shape and bristol fashion just two days later. Then a rag and bone man called. We had nothing for him. BUT! I spotted over three feet of inch and a half of pristine copper pipe on his cart.

"How much will you take for the copper pipe?" I asked.

"I'm not selling, scrap copper is at an all time high."

"Name your price."

"A pound."

"I'll give you ten bob."

"Done."

The car tail pipe was 'going' where it curved over the back axle. The original fitted 'inside' the silencer, I reckoned with a bit of fiddling and a clamp the new copper pipe would fit 'outside'. Five doors down the street was a builder's yard. I took my pipe down and had words with the foreman. Permission granted. I filled the pipe with builder's sand, bunged both ends up. and wrapped it around a suitable tree awaiting the attentions of the saw. I tugged and sweated at the two ends without any movement. The foreman came over. "Thee get thi boddy at yon end, and 'ang on," he instructed. He all but pulled me off my feet, but within minutes we had the 'U' bend just where I needed it. I took out the bungs and put the sand back on his pile. "It'll cost you a pint at The Hare," he warned. I nodded in happy agreement. Four saw cuts, an exhaust clamp, a bracket for the back end, the engine sounded like a very angry wasp. Smashing.

Now the time for a test drive, every mechanics prayer time, it sounded super and performed very well. I buzzed it up Putney Hill, turned round, and 'howled' it back down again. Beaming with self satisfaction.

As I crossed the Mill Dam bridge, a familiar tall slender female form was walking towards me. Her once very angular face had softened during the years I had been away, she was quite lady like now. I pulled up, parked, and went across to say hello. "It is Jane?" Without a single thought to my appearance.

She looked puzzled for a few seconds. "Oh, it's you," her deep, almost masculine voice had not changed at all. "I had heard you were in selling now, no one told me that you were still repairing cars."

"I'm not, this is my own little tub that needed some attention. Sorry about my filth, but I just had to road test it to make sure."

We had attended the same school, whilst I was in the local Air Training Corps, she had been a member of the local girls equivalent group. We had known each other for years, dances, socials, out walking. To be honest, she had never looked on me in a favourable light in those days. I suppose I was more uncouth than ever then.

We chatted away on the 'memories', then found out that we were both free this evening. "Would she like a run in my refurbished motor?"

It took her a long time to answer, my pride was hurt. A young, free, healthy male on offer. I dug in and tried again.

"I've been out five nights in a row, my hair needs washing."

If it's not available, I want it. She eventually agreed to wash the hair tomorrow night. I promised to pick her up as soon after half past seven as I could, pointing out that my filthy condition would need considerable attention.

I arrived less than a quarter of an hour late, she came out of the front door as soon as I pulled up. We set off, Putney, Larburton lakes, Lime Tree Avenue, wondering where on earth I should take her, now she was in the little motor. She had mentioned she did not mind an occasional drink, but could not see any point in sitting in a pub all night. Dilemma. It had been a reasonable day, but now, grey, over cast, slight drizzle. Not at all pleasant driving for the sake of driving. Then I remembered Fred, whom I had not seen for some considerable time. We had served in India together, a small man, with wavy hair, a very zany sense of humour, BUT! Every alternate Saturday when we were paid, he would blow the lot in one terrific booze up. Yet another dilemma.

I related the facts to her, and asked her opinion. A little uncertain, but she thought we could give him a try, IF in fact he had the humour I spoke of. I looked on her with a different light, as I did not remember her being a giggle a minute type. Fred had lost his Mum very early on, and had been brought up by his Mum's sister, who in turn was married to an (apparent) dour Scotsman. All a front, he was terrific company. All this cheered Jane, and we carried on to 'Auntie's'.

Fred had gone out, Auntie knew not where, but she made us promise that 'find him or not', we must return for a 'bite of supper'.

Fred seemed to prefer the roughest of rough pubs, so I went to what I thought was the worst, hoping he was not available. No such luck, he was 'chatting up' a real tarty looking blonde scrubber. I felt sure that she had applied her make up with a four inch brush. Even this early, it was bedlam, the pub was packed with people, noise, and cigarette smoke.

But, as soon as he spotted me, he dropped the blonde like a hot coal and came over. I dragged him outside, telling him what I thought of his taste in pubs. He mentioned a newly opened place, it had been a large country house, a pub now, but the owners intended it to be a good hotel. Off we went, to be fair to Fred it was too far out of town for him to walk.

It was very 'top drawer' suited Jane admirably. We had a pleasant couple of hours. Fred's zany humour really suited Jane, for a change those two did most of the chatting. We then had coffee, with superb bread and dripping sandwiches served on a silver platter. Scrumptious. The owner explained he intended doing meals as soon as possible. He had cooked a good size piece of beef, his wife had suggested they try beef and or dripping sandwiches. What a very good idea.

It must have been nine thirty when we dropped Fred at home. He started to plead. "Come in and say hello to Aunt and Uncle before you go."

I told him that we were invited to supper. With a happy grin, he led us in. What a table was already laid, I (almost) wished I had not had those sandwiches. Uncle was in great form telling of the adventures of Scots.

One about Hadrian on his wall to keep the Scots out. The 'haggis bashers' had stolen two sheep, so Hadrian he upped his guards to twenty, two more sheep gone, guards bloody and muddy, he upped his guards to a hundred.

Two more sheep went and all the centurions returned battered and bleeding. The man in charge complained. "You did nae tell us that there were two of them."

It really was late by the time we could get away. The little car buzzed with its healthy note to the level crossing on the A6420. Gates closed, we had to wait for a coal train. It chuffed it's way across, the crossing keeper wound his handle to open the gates, with a nonchalant wave to him, I drove on. Till a cloud of steam obliterated my view. The wipers did not clear it, it was inside as well. Almost 'feeling' my way to the side of the road, I switched off, nipped out, and picked up the bonnet. Something like hades, I wafted with my hands to no effect, so I passed Jane the torch out of the driver's pocket, then used my 'window cloth' to flap the steam away Whilst Jane held the 'seeing' torch for me. Problem solved, the rusty remains of a core plug, steaming in the engine block. Tool bag out, a screwdriver soon levered out the remnants, a broken off hacksaw blade cleaned out the rust residue. We then both spread out all the coins we had between us on the running board. A two shilling piece was just a touch too big. But with all the luck in the world I had put an old bearing in the tool bag, it worked as a base to rest the edge of the coin on, a sharp blow in the middle with hammer and a brass drift, 'bellied' the coin just enough to fit the hole. In it went, and a few sharp taps with the hammer sealed it.

The radiator swallowed all my spare bottle of water without noticing, I trotted to and fro to a part filled dyke by torch light, getting almost a quarter bottle of water each trip. Probably a dozen such trips had the radiator full again. Bonnet down, switched on and she purred into life. With tongue in cheek and baited breath I nursed the little car back home.

Her Mother, late as it was, was still waiting up. She listened with some doubt to my explanations, but I like to think that my filthy hands did add credence to our story.

The following morning I drained the filthy ditch water out, to refill with clean tap water. When I removed the radiator filler cap. out jumped a perfectly formed miniature frog!!!

I thought later, IF it had not been the middle of the night, IF a garage had been available, I could have bought the correct core plug for say, two pence. But I must say, many years later, the two bob piece was still in place, in pristine condition, and of course, no rust.

On such a dodgy beginning, a relationship built up between us. Jane would wait, no matter how late, for my return from work, she was good company, had a host of friends, all very musical. So she educated me musically, whilst I introduced her to the joys of motoring.

Chapter 22
If It Breaks, Drop It

All bills now paid, Mrs Wells' bedroom was filling up, I
now had a half gross of boxes stored therein. But I was
still short on shirts. I had never before realised. People
hardly ever bought for the future, they bought when they
needed to. If they wanted a shirt that you did not have,
they bought elsewhere. To be honest, I had not realised to
what extent choice added up to. Say ten different sizes in
first the obligatory white of course, followed by cream
and blue. Then you got the ones wanting stripes, broad
and narrow, neat checks, tattersall checks, in all colours
of course. I had almost one hundred and fifty shirts in
stock, only one of each type, size, and colour. A box of
each would have cost a fortune, so I had to buy singly
and pay extra. Even so, at least once a week some silly
ass needed one that was not in my stock.

A second cousin caused a problem, he wanted a
small neat check in blue, size fifteen. (Not a popular size)
Try as I might, I had problems. Van Heuson did do one,
but they were an agency only line. In my efforts to suit I
bought fourteen oddments. It took the cousin four weeks
to pay what he called cash, leaving me with all those
shirts in a slow selling size to make less than ten shillings
profit. AND he expected cash discount.!

Still, I had no regular rounds, it was all sort of 'bitty
bobby'. Not at all economical, but as yet no one village or
district did enough trade to warrant a half days
concentrated work.

The nasty, bad tempered owner neighbour had died

some years ago. The whole property was bought by a nice old couple, for a while all was sweetness and delight. Then poor old hubby got prostate cancer and died. The widow put it all on the market and went to live with her daughter.

A queer group of four limp wristed chaps bought it and announced that they would turn next door into a cafe.

The four seemed to work in shifts, day and night. Banging, scraping, drilling, whilst they fitted ovens, grills, shelves, sinks, finishing up with a waist high fireplace in the bedroom. The biggest, a large man with a huge beard had a voice like a foghorn shouting at intervals both day and night.

"It's no good Cecil, we shall have to scrub it again."

Had it not been so serious, under a different heading it might have been funny. But Dad, needed, and liked his sleep. His temper grew shorter day by day. He had to get up about four a.m. After his numerous accidents, plus his age. He found the hurly burly of hundreds of rushing colliers too much. His back injury needed to be nursed, and his foot without a sole offered no 'cushion' to protect his back. For some time now he had been on what the Colliery Company called a 'light job'. Driving the main haulage engine which powered the belt taking coal back to the pit bottom. Going early not only cleared that problem, but it also allowed the man on the previous shift to get home earlier.

Back home, the previous property owners had created a little rose arbour facing their back door. This new lot put a frame round it to enclose it all with chicken wire, in it they installed a half wild monkey. In no time at all it had learned to swing in the climbing rose trees without collecting any thorns in its hands. That winter was dreadfully cold. The poor little thing almost went wild when Mum tossed a newly boiled potato to it. It juggled the still steaming potato from hand to hand before chewing it with great relish. We had a little excitement when the monkey bit a piece out of the big fellow's arm.

Their next acquisition was a Police reject Alsation, it was equally wild and unpredictable. They put a wire between two posts the full length of the yard, slotted it through the loop of the dog lead. So giving it a to and fro run of around forty yards. Depending on its mood, it would either come to nuzzle you, or take a piece out. If the Police could not train it, what chance had they? Needless to say, trips to and from the car were now fraught with hazards. I have always been a 'dog' man, but that animal was a different story. As a mate used to tell me. "It's as dodgy as a two pound note."

After many months of the noise, the cafe opened. BUT! They stayed open while ever drunks needed feeding, it got to its worst just after ten thirty p.m. Friday and Saturday nights especially. They had to ban some particular rowdy gangs, so they marched through our front door instead. For the first time ever, we had to lock it. The following Saturday a very irate mob were refused entry. As our front doors were only feet apart they battered on our door.

Dad snapped, he instructed me to go round by the back gate and come from behind them, IF! His final instructions were IF, they want trouble, pick on the biggest with the most mouth. I did as instructed, and waited just outside the gate. Needless to say full of trepidation. There must have been at least forty in the crowd. Dad opened our front door, they surged forward. He held his hands up. This is a private house, it has bugger all to do with the cafe, will you all please go before I call the police. That is what he meant anyway, but it was nothing like the message he passed on.

A big burly youth at the front squared up to him, mouthing obscenities. Dad told him to go in, 'pit talk'.

"Why I'll," the big chap started and swung his fist. Not quick enough, Dad swayed away from the punch, whilst his own right fist caught big boy a real purler, right on the 'sweet spot'. He went out like a light. A big ginger haired youth in front of me surged forward, mouthing.

"I tapped him on the shoulder and said "Excuse Me." He turned, open mouthed with surprise. I shut it with the best punch I have ever thrown. He back pedalled two steps before crashing down on his back. The 'boing' as his head hit the tarmac could be heard all down the now quiet street.

"Are you all going to bugger off now, or does anyone else want a taste?" from Dad. They all filed away in silence, leaving the two bodies where they lay. As if by magic, just as soon as they had all gone, a Policeman arrived. (Mum had phoned the station) Dad had short shrift for him, explained the situation, instructed "See to them." Turned and went back in the house. I went in the same way as I had gone out, round the back. Arrived in the room to see Dad flexing his already swelling

knuckles, and saying to Mum. "There's 'ope fer 'im yet."
Nodding in my direction. Whilst lighting his pipe he
gave me instructions for the morrow.

"Report it to the station, ask for support next wik, as
when they've got another belly full of Dutch courage
they'll be back."

The Police Station was like a grave Sunday morning,
not a sign of life. So I went again on Monday. With
hindsight, I realised how many were in the gang, it could
so easily have meant hospital for Dad and I.

"Would the Police let us have some back up, and
could they possibly let me have a knuckle duster?"

The Sergeant almost laughed aloud.

"No way, we have a drawer full, it's my job getting
them off the streets, not re issuing them. The two you
clobbered had a night in the cells, who hit the ginger
one?"

I had to admit that it was I.

"You don't need a knuckle duster, he's in hospital
with concussion."

We were all full of tension the following Saturday.
Dad suggested I stood behind the open yard gate again,
in case. A mass used the Cafe, but no trouble. Just after
eleven a patrol man walked past and swung his lantern
my way. "What yer doin' there, come on out." I did so
and explained the fracas of the week previous.

He nodded in understanding. "I saw it all, I was off
duty going home the other side of the street."

"Why did you not help?"

"I've just said, I was off duty."

My teeth bared in anger. "I would've always helped

225

the police in time of trouble, but if that's your bloody attitude, count me out."

I shut the yard gate and stormed in seething.

Possibly Wednesday the following week whilst I was rushing breakfast, a knock on the door the letter box rattled, followed by a solid sort of thump. I rushed to the door and opened it, not a single soul in the street. Near the door mat was a good quality manila envelope, I opened it. A very nice workmanlike knuckle duster.

All of this was getting to be beyond a joke. Dad instructed everyone to look out for a new home. A pit house in a terrace had never appealed to him, he had dreamed of a little place in the country that the wind could blow right round.

Price was also a problem, we had never ever 'owned' property. One day at work a customer mentioned that the wood and asbestos bungalow next door was to come up for sale. A large garden, heavy clay land, garage and outside toilet made from colliery belting. I was not impressed, worried about Mum, but Dad as usual went for it like a bull at a gate. Down two steps from the kitchen door to the toilet, wash house, and coal house. I cringed for poor Mum. BUT! Dad was in charge as always.

Wood and asbestos construction, so no mortgage available, price Nine Nine Five. We did not have that in total between us. Dad's tin off the cupboard was emptied, I rustled up forty pounds, and Uncle Bob stumped up an undisclosed sum.

It needed decorating inside and out. Anyone who could or would help was roped in. Every available evening and all weekends saw the revival of slave traffic.

After a hard Sunday grafting at it, Mum, Dad, self and Jane were starting a very late tea, tired and filthy. In walked Eric. "I've got a flat," he announced.

"Wait till I've finished eating and I will give you a hand," I growled through a mouthful.

He looked astonished till light dawned. "I mean a flat to live in not a puncture flat."

"You already have a posh bungalow."

"Not for me, for you and Jane." My turn for the brain wheels to slowly function. We did enjoy each other's company, we did have all the 'perks' of a long relationship, but neither of us had ever mentioned wedding bells. With a bump, my belly dropped into my boots. I looked across at her. Her head was down, feeding like there was no tomorrow due.

Eric bubbled on, impervious. "It's got all you want, an' it's only a pound a week, plus rates. I've got a key, we can go and look at it, now if you like."

That brought Jane alive. "I'm not going anywhere in this condition."

He was still on cloud nine. "I'll run you home while he gets changed." It appears that whilst Jane was washing and changing, her Mother questioned. "Where do you think you are taking her at this time of night? She's tired out and needs to be abed."

A happy Eric informed he had got us a flat so that I would now be able to marry and make an honest women of her daughter. He never would ever make the diplomatic corps.

One door only, straight up a flight of stairs, then a

long passage, off which in order, Kitchen, Bedroom, Bathroom, then at the end a nice large lounge. Eric was really keen, whilst he shot from room to room. I was busy pacing the length of the passage and stairs. Needless to say it all was in desperate need of decoration.

Jane noticed my furrowed brow and asked what? "I'm working the cost of twenty two inch stair and runner carpet for this lot."

"Start again, I will want at least twenty seven inch. Preferably thirty six."

Eric dropped us off at our respective homes, still chortling, by now all parents were in bed. Other than telling them we had not said a word to anyone.

Off first thing in the morning buying to the City. My mind 'should have' been on my order book. But more engrossing was the little I had in the bank, and what this lot was going to cost me. At long last I cleared my mind and decided we would discuss it all when we met. Back home, all bought goods spread out whilst I priced and packed when Mum came back from the shops'

"I've put two wedding presents on your bed. Mrs P. and your Aunt Ethel brought them." Then almost as an afterthought added. "You're thirty two, it's time you did."

I got round to Jane's about on time, looking a bit pale and wan I guess. Her mum proudly announced she already had three presents delivered. We called back at my home. Dad said "I will buy you a room carpet." (He never did, nor did he attend our little wedding.)

"I canna afford to have a shift off," his reason.

It was a private little mid week do, just a dozen friends came back to her home for a bite, plus of course the vicar.

"What would you like to drink?" I asked him.

"A whisky."

I poured what I thought was a good one. "Anything in it?"

"Yes, another whisky if you please."

Married Thursday morning, off to a very soggy Lake District for two and a half days, back to work on Monday morning.

Mid day, a message delivered. "Would I please call on a Mrs. Shirman in the Alley." I went almost straight away.

A small pigeon chested lady, with piercing, almost black eyes, a very firm set to her mouth and jaw, arms folded firmly under her over ample bust. "I've been told that you're reasonably priced, straight, and a pleasure to deal with." I gave one of my semi naughty replies agreeing with all she said.

My 'mucky' humour did not meet with any approval at all, her very set face left me in no doubt. Then a small, unobtrusive man sort of sidled in round the back door, he seemed unsure if he was doing right.

How right that he was wrong. She turned on him. "Go back in the garden, I am doing business with this man." He did not sidle out, he fled. She carried on. "I married him," with a sniff towards the back door.

"Twenty odd years ago, he bought a packet of them 'thingies', three in it there were. He had used all three in less than a week, so I said to him Friday morning, don't waste your money on any more of them, you'll not be needing them, I'm getting two single beds for the two rooms."

She then ordered two complete sets of single bedding and pillow cases, all to match, but two 'different' bedspreads. With a stiff upper lip I delivered the following week and was paid cash.

Chapter 23
Countrywise

By now I had a half night of calls on Fridays, five and a half hours on Saturdays, a couple of hours Mondays, and nothing else. Although I needed time to buy and price, a spare afternoon for oddments and special deliveries, the car needed to be kept clean and serviced and so on, I still needed more work. A few weeks ago, Freddie in 'The Hare' had suggested it might be good to stretch my wings a little and get away from the colliery villages. He rightly pointed out that colliers can be a stroppy lot. (Still a lot of unrest among the militants) Little strikes could ruin my collections and income. Any such problems could see me in trouble. Rightly again, he pointed out that farmers were too busy to shop, they usually lived in villages away from town. Did not spend in the pub or the bookies to the same extent. The more I thought, the more I realised the benefit of education. (Freddy was a school headmaster.)

The very next Tuesday, I cleared the car and really filled it with goods that might sell to a 'catch' trade. It took longer than I expected, it was after lunch time when I eventually set off into the wilds of the countryside.

"It's hardly changed at all," I mused to myself as the little car ground its way up Pockling Hill in second gear. When I was a school boy, this area had been Dad's happy hunting Saturdays. He was mad keen on fox hunting. Every possible chance in season he was with the hounds. Feet, cycle, motor cycle, little car, the better the transport, the further he could get. Mum and I had no choice, we had to join in. He had now retired, had to stop driving, and was struggling with his large garden of heavy clay land.

He was still happy with his little bungalow with the wind blowing all round it. No good at all to Mum of course. He had spent on alterations. A bedroom had been altered into a bathroom and toilet. New mains water had been laid on, they were now connected to a main sewer, and for the first time ever they could flush indoors.

Of course I was now saddled with all shopping trips, or to the pit for his pitiful pension plus any other whims he may get. He still never asked, he instructed when and where he should be taken. The modern highway code was ignored. "Pull up theer. Theer, theer, theer," as I swept past the No Parking area, HE wanted me to stop at.

All this was going through my mind as the car climbed steadily, then breasted the hill. I gasped. It can't be the SAME Hay Stack? I stopped to savour it.

Same size, shape, and place, looking tired, yes, but? was it the same? During the war, as a teenager, and a member of the local Air Training Corps, the village had organised a 'Wings for Victory Week'. The big final Saturday night bash had been a dance in the village hall. ALL the serving forces from miles around had been invited. Two guards units from two of the local Abbeys. Field Ambulance from the Park. WAAF and RAF from two air stations. The last lot had included a gaggle of W.A.A.F.S. from R.A.F. Mossingboro. After the dance, I and a few mates had escorted the cycling W.A.A.F.S. back home on our bikes. We had all stopped on a superb moonlight night for the most hilarious romp in the hay.

The W.A.A.F. I had partnered had proved to be learned, gentle, kind and understanding, whilst she had taken my virginity. "I wonder where she is now."

Reverie over, I re started. Nicked the box into second, and wound the engine up, round the next corner, then had to drop the anchor's on, sharpish! The road was full of hounds and riders.

"A good job Dad is not here." I thought as I sat to watch.

"Am I in your way?" As a lady rider approached, leading her mount.

"Ectuarly no, the blarsted fox crossed the road, into that ditch, through a small hole in the wire netting. The pack was so close on its heels, all were trying to get through at once. It was very much a no no. The road was full of hounds, my horse tried to stop in mid air, she just torpled me orf."

"Oh dear, Ave yer ot yer?"

"I do beg your pardon?

"Sorry, have you hurt yourself?" I repeated in a more suitable accent.

"Ectuarly no, I fell on a mass of bleddy hounds that broke my fall. Do you have any knowledge of where the horse boxes are?"

"None the way I have come, they may be forard in Paxton. Or over East at Buxford." Waving towards to the East without a clue.

"Thanks awfully," she gushed over her shoulder as she mounted without effort and instructed her horse to "walk on."

I looked and tried to work out the situation. The little

old cottage I remembered had been extended. The owner had used the dyke bottom to bed his chicken wire under high posts. 'Thanks,' said Reynard as he had dug out the soft mud. It seems he had scarpered out of a similar situation the other side. Hounds were scrabbling at both holes and not doing very well.

"Ees bin 'ere before, knowed 'is road through. Townies don't know how clever they are."

I turned at the familiar voice

"Good Lord, it's Harry, not seen you in years."

"Weer's yer Dad then?"

"At home I guess."

"What am you doing 'ere without 'im?"

"I came to do some work, never gave the hounds a thought."

"Don't let 'im know, 'ee might kill you."

"He might at that, now he does not drive, he's had to miss out on hunting."

"All the more reason for doin' you damage." Harry almost looked delighted at the prospect. "'Ow is the auld bugger, it's many years sin I seed 'im."

With a slight start I realised just how long since Dad had a day with the hounds. "He had a few minor shunts in the car, realised that he had passed it, and packed it in. He's not told me to bring him for ages, he might have realised I'm short of time."

"He still tells then? No thought to ask." I looked, deep in thought, without any attempt to reply. He went on. "Suppose it's a bit late to expect 'im to alter ner?" Then before he turned to go he spoke his own thoughts. "Done think I've ever knowed nobody as keen on 'untin' as yer Dad."

By now the hounds had torn the dyke bottoms to shreds and were straggling over the fields towards Kneeser. A few of the earlier ones were trying to get in full cry, but it all sounded half hearted. I thought for a while about 'following', but between Kneeser and here, very few roads. In any case, Reynard was always likely to double back. Not at all suitable 'following' country. With a sigh of semi regret I pressed on to Paxton.

Thinking about work again. I've never done any canvassing, how do I set about it? Dad used to have friends here, but could I pester them? "Hello er um , do you remember Jack? I'm his lad." It did not sound at all right. On such thoughts I travelled the four miles or so further. Past the fork, then the Church, ignored the left turn and went down hill. OOOOPS. It was full. Grooms, horseboxes, followers on foot, horse back, and pushbikes. Twenty or so cars, riders changing mounts, grooms having a crafty fag. I had never ever seen the village so full. With great care I trickled through the throng till I found a tight space to park. Got out, locked up, and sauntered to the farm on the right fork corner where most seemed to be gathered.

"Thought yer were werkin'." Harry again. "Ee's bin through another 'en run, two 'oles agin, one in one ert. Bin ere afore 'ee as, knows is road around. Alf at yon farm yonder in't 'alf mad, lost no end of 'ens ee 'as. 'Ees gone in fer pliers to cut an 'ole in't wire. Whoops that's torn it, no pliers needed."

The pushing mass of hounds had broken two fence posts off at the point where they entered the soil. Some went under, some over, they sprayed over the field, noses down, searching for scent.

Harry and I entered the yard, Alf the farmer, pliers in hand was swearing at the remnants of his fence and the world in general. Then, on a typical hunt day, the rain came down in torrents. We backed in to a loose box and lit up. It was raining far too hard to make a run for it. Harry's bike leaning against the wall was well and truly awash.

We smoked, chatted about Dad, the old days, the changes in the village. Harry advised who and where to call. Who had cars and would not need me, who had children and maybe would. "As you remember it was all farms and farm workers, now the townies are coming in, knocking things dern, sticking bits on, it'll never be the same again." Then he thought. "Tell thee wot, dunna call ner, them what's bin at wok will be tired and 'ungry, them wot's bin 'untin' 'll be code an' wet. Cum early next wik, I'll put word round that you're due.

The rain eased just as quickly as it had started, I thanked him for his help, advice, and opinion. As I set off for the car I turned to wave goodbye. Then I saw it. Above his head, on a beam about ten foot high, a foot of tongue panting away was the fox. Y'know, I could have sworn it winked as it lay recovering...

In the morning I had to empty and refill the car, what a silly waste of time yesterday. For some time now I had been getting headaches, the doctor had advised me to get the eyes tested, today was the day of my appointment. Although his consulting rooms were in the town, the optician and I originated from the same village. But! his Father was a chemist, mine was a collier, my school was council, his school was grammar, as a boy he had a pony, I did not even get a bike till I was fourteen. In spite of, we had always got on well. One thing led to another, and I admitted I had every intention of writing a book about my traumatic amusing life. This got an admission out of him that he had always 'intended', but so far had not even started. But he did tell me of an amusing incident when he took local photos for the Church Magazine. An old couple were due to celebrate their diamond wedding HE had been asked to photograph the pair of them. All set and ready, she asked.

"Bill weer's yer teeth?"

"Upstairs why?"

"Your 'avin' yer photo took. 'Ere borrow my top set." Took them out and passed them over.

He decided I did need spectacles, but I only needed to use them when I wanted to see?? I could take them off at all other times???? When fitted I went to show Mum, she decided that in view of my expanding waistline, balding head, bespeckled look, I was no longer her young lad, BUT ! I still retained my sense of humour.

"But I'm still odd Mum," I complained. "Forty three chest, thirty three waist, inside leg twenty nine, nothing 'off the peg' fits me."

With a chuckle, she ruffled my thinning locks and admitted.

"You always were lad."

On my way back home I intended calling at the village Post Office for stamps. I pulled up in the lay by before it, about to get out, froze and shrank in the seat. Two people getting out of a Ford five hundredweight van in front. My ex manager, Churchill, and a school class mate. Class mate gives the wrong impression, we were in the same class, mates we were not. Kenneth Williamson. I mused. An unctuous youth, as phoney as a two pound note. He would drop anyone 'innitt' to save his own skin. Greasy, swarthy, thick dark hair that almost covered his forehead, very unsavoury.

They seemed to be having an argument, after much head movement, and arm waving, Churchill got out and went round to the house back door of the Post office. Kenneth got out of the passenger side, into the driver's side to turn the van round, not a lot of space, he shunted too and fro, then backed into the car behind. Scrunch, tinkle tinkle of broken glass. (Head lamp glasses shattered, and a crease in the radiator shell.)

He got out, all furtive, looked at the damage, produced pen and paper and wrote. Tucked the paper under the windscreen wiper and drove off at high speed.

Curious, I crept over to have a look at the note.

"Sorry! I have just backed into your car, anyone watching will think I am leaving my name and address. BUT I'M NOT!

Some people and things will never ever change.

238

Chapter 24
Rural Humour

It was my 'country' day again, how time flies. I now had twenty credit customer's, all with a very low balances, but depending on the luck of the day I could get some good cash trade. No doubt, they are a careful lot out here in the sticks. But they did talk, word was getting around that I was reliable and reasonably priced. I had many times mentally thanked Freddy for his good advice.

One should not have favourites, in life or business, but we all do. One account I really did like. Jesse Richards and family. His farm was at what was known as West End. Had Jessie been in the North East, he would no doubt have been dubbed as a 'Canny Bugger'. He always seemed to do the right things at the right time. He was red faced, corpulent, with sandy thinning hair, his wife, large, well fed, and a glutton for work. A daughter, maybe fourteen or fifteen, two sons around eight or ten respectively. The two young lads were adept at getting out of work, but every one else seemed to be ready and able to turn their hands to anything. I had seen all but the lads gathering fruit, stripping geese and cockerels, digging the garden, 'plashing' hedges, painting and washing up. On one pre Christmas occasion I caught Jesse up to the elbows in washing up water with his hands still lathered in paint, his wife outside knee deep in goose feathers.

The daughter 'could have' been dishy, 'could have' was not fair, she was. But I had never ever seen her other than in old clothes working like a beaver. Even when the so called day chores were complete and she sat. The knitting needles flew at her nimble fingers. I used to think what superb wife material she would make, but the modern young men were more inclined to sniff around the dressed up dolly birds. I fleetingly thought of Eric's wife, then dismissed the thoughts with a wry grin.

I knocked on the door of West End House and walked in.

"You've timed it just right again Ron," the daughter smiled as she carried a mass of dirty pots to the sink and returned with my usual cup of tea.

"Come on you two, finish your meal so that I can wash up and get on with my work." The two lads sat on opposite sides of the table, gazing at two only pieces of cake left on a centre plate.

"Can we?"

"Yes, I will make more after I've washed up."

With a deft swoop, the smaller of the two snaffled the larger piece of cake.

Big brother moaned. "You should always take the smaller piece, you've been told often enough."

"Which bit would you have taken had you been quick enough?"

"The smallest of course," with a side long glance in my direction to see if he had impressed .

"Well shurrup then, that's what you've got," munching with glee on his 'prize'.

Difficult, but I managed to keep a straight face. "Who's helping with the washing up?" I asked.

Both rushed for the part open door. Oldest. "I've got ter muck ert." Youngest. "I'm cleaning my bike."

"Thanks for that," the daughter turned from the sink with a shy smile. "We don't know where he gets it from, he really can be a cheeky young monkey, but I'm better off with them from under my feet so that I can get my work done."

"I did need to laugh," I had to admit. "But dare not let them see me."

"I'm afraid Dad is in the dog house again," she carried on, her pretty little face creasing with worry.

"Why, what's he done this time?" Wondering if it was yet another astute move by Jesse.

"It's dad really, I was crying last night in bed, best not tell anyone though," with an anxious look at me.

I almost blurted. "You should know me by now. Do you want to tell me?"

"I really must tell someone," she was close to tears. "Remember when Dad bought me that young hunter? He thought and hoped I would make a show jumper."

Nodding, I had to wonder if I had been wise to ask.

"Dad's car is clapped out, he needs another one, all we have to sell and raise the money is my Peggy. Alf Crow down town end said he would have her for his daughter Daisy. She was riding it in their paddock last night, foot in a rabbit hole, she broke her arm, it broke a leg and had to be put down." Tears flowed, with a sobbing "sorry" she fled.

Nonplussed, I finished my tea, put the cup and saucer in the sink bowl, and stood like a lemon. What do I do or say?

Thankfully she soon returned, face freshly washed, but still looking rather pale and wan. "Sorry about that, you won't tell anyone will you?"

My head was shaking in what I hoped was a reassuring manner. But thinking about Jesse's reputation about always selling things just before they either broke or died. "He can't be blamed for a horse putting its foot in a rabbit hole. I'm sure he's straight."

"He is," with a look of appreciation. "You did hear when he sold his old bull to Ron Free?"

I had to shake my head.

She almost managed a giggle. "A while ago our old bull got to be too old." She was blushing I realised. "You do know what I mean?"

I looked blank.

"You do know what bulls are for?" With a pitiful look at my ignorance.

Light dawned, it was my turn to colour up. I muttered "Sorry."

"Dad had to go to the cattle market on a terrible day, only a few had braved the weather. A two year old Friesian cross was on offer without a reserve, no one bid, so he made a daft offer and it was accepted. He reckoned he could get more than he had paid at the knacker's yard, but all seems to be well, we have a good calf and two cows in calf. Ron Free heard and offered to buy our old one. Dad said it was old, but Ron was keen. I don't know what Dad charged him. In no time at all Ron was complaining it did not seem interested. So Dad told him to go to the Vet, tell him he had our old bull, and ask for some pills. Just give him one the morning of the day he was to work. Ron, as usual a worry, asked how he would know he had the right pills."

She was struggling to control and stifle the giggles by now, I was puzzled to say the least.

Then in a rush she gabbled her punch line. "Dad said they are a pale blue as big as your thumb nail and have a slight taste of peppermint." Control all gone now, she exploded with laughter, I had to join in. Surprised as I was. The kitchen door flew open, and in walked her Mother.

"Now then what's amusing you two?" She questioned, looking very stern.

"Oh hello Mrs Richards, I did not know you were out," brain whirring to think of something.

"I did not want to, too busy, but I had to. Jesse sent me to Market to get him a new sieve, his old one is full of holes." That did it, Daughter and I were helpless, Mother looked puzzled. Daughter eventually explained with great difficulty.

"He meant holes that should not be there. Now what was amusing you two?"

"Oh 'er I was just telling her about a Miner in Hollerton who has just died."

"Nothing funny in that." she snapped.

I pressed on. "He was a real bad un, bone idle, did not go to work and did nothing at home, spent all his time in either the bookies or pub. Now that he has gone, his wife has had his ashes made in to an egg timer, now all she needs to do to make him of use is to turn him over."

Her face 'almost' relaxed, I wondered if it had registered, the daughter flashed me a look of gratitude and busied herself at the sink.

All bustle, Mrs Richards took off her coat, hung it behind the door, requested that I bring an assortment of bedside mats next time, and pushed me through the door. "Sorry! I'm very busy."

I walked slowly back to the car, deep in thought about Jesse. I had heard he sold his old binder to Jack Free, within hours the seat spring snapped and the sheet split. BUT! Jesse had cut all Jacks harvest for him and not charged. Then it was rumoured that when his Collie bitch had been in season, he had tied her to a tree all night in a local spinney, wondering if a fox would mate with her. He reasoned that the good sense of a Collie crossed with the craft of a fox would be some dog. "I must ask around if anything resulted."

Next call, well down the village, old Sam and his lady, a sweet old couple, both in tremendous shape considering they were well over eighty. Sam was small, of slight build he might on a good day weigh nine stone. Almost white sparse hair, an always smiling 'outdoor' face. His lady wife was even smaller in height, but very round, with clean hair as white as driven snow, her skin was as smooth as any baby's botty. Normally faces creased in happy smiles. NOT today.

She looked careworn and Sam looked to be stones heavier

"What on earth have you got young man?" I questioned as I stepped through the door.

"Yer can 'ave 'em if yer want 'em," he offered. Eyes still glinting with humour.

"NO THANK YOU," I refused.

"Ester sin yon big wood pile in Neeser wood?"

"Yes, the hunt killed out of it when I was a lad, Jacklin 'blooded' me as no junior riders were present." Sam just nodded as though he knew. (He probably did)

"It's bin theer fer years and years, thought it were time I shifted it. I got theer abert seven and begun, a few bits at a time like. I'd moved quite a bit, when a wasp stung me on me tab, thought nowt on it and went back for more. Think I upset 'em, never sin so many afore. Well I canna run like I uster, an' a looronem got me afore I gorraway."

His lady butted in, "I've counted over five hundred stings, had to pull some out with tweezers, 'ope I've not missed any, the silly old devil is always worrying me sick. He won't let me lather him with washing blue or T.C.P. He reckons he won't go out coloured or stinking."

"I don't think he will be out for a few days," I offered, he really did worry me.

"You know Sam, wild horses won't keep him in."

His puffy face creased in a huge grin, whilst he nodded in agreement.

"I bet they hurt."

"Well purrit this road, I'm warm all ovver."

I suggested the Dr. (Waste of time) T.C.P. (Dunna want ter stink) so thought it best to retire from the scene.

We shall never ever see the likes again, thoughts as I slowly went back to the car. In the bad old days before the war. Sam had been scything the road side on a boiling hot day. He stopped for moments to divest his coat and waistcoat. The local estate agent arrived on horse back and hit Sam over the back with his riding crop for slacking. Sam could now take coat and waistcoat off and

245

replace them without missing a single scythe stroke.

Only last year a local farmer's seed drill had broken.
Sam had hand sown a twenty acre field on that heavy un
yielding clay land. I had lost many hours sleep trying to
work just out how many miles he would have walked.
Only recently I had caught him ditching. (Cleaning out
the overgrown grass and mud from the ditch bottom.) A
nice warm day, but Sam with coat and waistcoat on
slinging shovels full of heavy semi wet mud on to the
field above. "Will this weather hold Sam?" I asked.

"Nay lad, it's no good asting me, them clever chaps
at th' B.B.C. knows all abert weather. But at abert six
every neet two auld craws flies ovver theer ta roost.
Today, them went at four, them knows, keep yer mac
'andy."

Within the hour, it was 'fair tippling darn', as Sam
would have put it...

I called at the joiner's shop for petrol. Joiner? Sorry,
he could tackle anything. Village undertaker, motor
mechanic, decorator. A happy ruddy face, everything
about him was round, face, belly, bum. A happy man
with two major faults. He never ever turned up on time,
and never ever had any money. He owed me, that's why I
called for petrol, I never paid for it, but crossed the
amount off his bill.

"Asteer bin ter t' market tern lately."

"No why?"

"Castle Motors as a grand big van in, just wot yo
need. Chap 'ad only 'ad it a few weeks. Reckon you
should goo and luke at it."

"By the way, t' ambulance man's wife wants ter see

yer."

Ambulance man, in a farm village? I was puzzling as I listened to instructions, then set off post haste.

A small, dainty women, gold, almost ginger hair, very very shy, she wanted some new bedding. I was writing her order in my little black book, this could be a useful account.

The door opened, in walked her husband, smallish, rotund, a mass of grey wavy hair. Little curly pipe gushing plumes of blue smoke. He nodded "ev'ning" to me, filled the kettle, put it on the fire, settled in an armchair, puffing contentedly on his pipe, looked intently at me.

"This is Mr Chapman," his wife introduced.

He literally bounded from his chair, shook hands (a dry firm shake) and in no time at all was back in his chair. How ever could such a little pipe produce so much smoke?

"Where did your brother work before and during the early part of the war?" Nothing wrong, it was a plain, direct question.

"No brothers, when they saw the results of the first try they never bothered again."

"Sorry, it's just that I was with a chap at the Portland Motor Co, thinner, more hair, and no specs."

I looked at him with more care. Imagined less weight, brown instead of grey hair, those still as ever laughing eyes. "Good Lord it's soup," I almost yelled as we bounded into each others' arms.

Len Till (hence soup) We had a constant battle for supremacy at the garage. I never ever came out on top, in spite of being eighteen months older. "I could have killed you that Saturday when you put a dirty oily tractor piston in my bike bag. I took a bird to the dance at the Abbey, she put her frock in my bike bag, it was ruined. Money material, and clothing coupons."

"Well, you had been trying to fix me all week, but I suppose I was naughty."

"Trying, trying, all I ever did was try. You nailed my snap bag to the tool stores board, dozens of nails, ruined the bag. So I put a sand bucket full in your drawer and stirred a gallon of old engine oil in for good measure."

Soup howled with laughter. "The foreman watched you do it and then told you to clean it out. I nearly wet myself."

So it went on, a good job it was my last call of the day. Even so, it was late when I got home. So many memories, so much laughter. I told him that I had refound Eric.

"Please arrange a meeting," he pleaded.

The next day had little or nothing planned, I spent some time thinking about the van in Town Daddo had mentioned. "What have I got to lose, I can but look?"

He was right, very delectable motor, much bigger, three or four times the room, slatted seats each side for my boxes, whilst the floor between would take rolls of lino or a carpet. Very low mileage, sliding doors, good turning circle, column gear change giving room for three bums on the front bench seat. The sin, 'desire' welled within. But????

The young, smooth tailor's dummy of a salesmen reeked of aftershave. But he gave me assurance it was a genuine low mileage snip and gave me the previous owner's name and phone number. I shot off to find a phone box very deep in thought. It would be possible, IF I could get a hundred for mine, IF I went without wages for a few weeks. So many IF'S, as always.

The previous owner assured me that all was genuine, the only reason it was for sale was that his wife refused to be taken out 'in a van'. SHE had MADE him buy an estate!!! The way women control lives.

Back to the garage, really bubbling, I dragged the salesman out to see mine for his price on it.

"Bloody Hell, it's older than I am, you don't expect to get anything for that do you?"

I had to admit, I got a hundred for it or it was all a waste of time.

Tooth sucking, head shaking he wished me luck in finding a dim clot that was thick, desperate, and with money to burn. Then he really hurt when he said another man was coming to see the van tomorrow.

I shot home at silly speeds, wrote on a post card, paid three pence to display it in the Post Office window, and went home to join Mum for lunch. She had to listen to it all whilst trying to eat.

Within minutes, a knock on the door. YIPPEE, a chap from the Alley interested. Meal forgotten I took him into the yard to see it. He just wanted a little 'runner' to take his kiddies to the sea side summer Sundays.

Thinking back, I now realise he looked at everything that did not matter, looked at nothing that did. Then asked "how many to the gallon?"

"High thirties pottering around, but last year I went

to North Wales and got fifty. (Very true, but I did not mention that I had broken two front road springs and needed to borrow garage space to fit new ones.)

All the work I had done was given in full detail, even showed him my two shilling piece, still clean and pristine.

"Will you take me a run in it?"

"Of course, jump in."

We buzzed round the country lanes, the 'rorty' exhaust throwing its tearing calico sound back at us from the trees, I all but put his head through the windscreen to demonstrate the brakes, and did him a hill start on Pockling Hill.

"Can I drive it?"

"Of course, and we changed seats. Within minutes he was out of it again, no way was I going to let my little car be treated so. Of course I have come across many bad drivers, but none as bad as this. NO WAY could he have my pride and joy unless I gave him a couple of hours tuition first. We agreed on after tea tonight, and he would bring the money!!!!!

After almost three hours the man was ringing with sweat, he suffered a full half hour stopping and starting, same again on gear changing, over an hour on reversing, then needed to be shown, lines on corners, breaking distances, speed on corners, eventually, still bad, but I was desperate for that hundred. He handed his bundle over, before giving the receipt I questioned. "Insurance?"

He looked blank.

I explained the rules.

"I shall be alright, it's only a couple of miles to the

Alley."

So I made him sign on his receipt and my piece of paper that he had been warned and that the onus was on him, 'IF'. The poor little car leapt through the gate and was gone.

Realisation!!! What if the van had been sold?

I went in to Phone Eric, told him what I had done, and asked for a lift first thing tomorrow. Silence! I waited than asked. "Did you hear me?"

"Yes, I'm thinking." More silence, then eventually. "The best I can offer is lunch time, the second best is to lend you my bike."

"It's twenty bloody miles and I have my own bike."

"How long since you rode it? I'll bet the tyres are buggered."

Deflated I realised, he was, as usual, right. I clammed up.

"What do you say it is?"

"A Bedford Workobus."

"Well, you've room in it to bring my bike back. I'll blow the tyres up now, wife will be in in the morning, she will let you have the shed key and my clips, I will meet you there as near to lunch time as I can. Sorry, will explain when I see you... Oh, it might be good sense to make sure it's still available before you start out."

Nonplussed, I put the phone down and went into our shed, my bike front tyre was pappy, the back flat! I pressed on the tread, a two inch split appeared, strands of the tube poked out. I went to bed to try and sleep. Not a chance, all I could see was the tooth sucking salesman and smell his aftershave, whilst he shook his head.

Up just after seven, breakfast, and phoned Castle Motors at eight. "Sales staff don't appear till nine," a brusque voice informed. Phoned at nine. "He's never ever on time, try later." I got him at nine fifteen.

"The other interested bloke is bringing his wife in this morning, it belongs to the first with the cash." Then he was called away from the phone.

I phoned Eric's home, no reply!! Finger nails down to the first knuckle I deliberated. Eric's home was over a mile away. Do I walk or try to borrow one nearer? I lit a shaky fag and someone knocked at the door.

Windswept and dishevelled, it was Eric's wife ON HIS RACING BIKE!!!! I took her face in both hands and kissed her full on the mouth. "I didn't know you cared," was her flustered reply. "Eric said you would appreciate delivery, I've enjoyed the ride, and can take it back if you don't want it."

"But I do I do, thank you so much."

Shouted to Mum I was off, put a duffle coat on, put Eric's clips on off his cross bar, kissed his wife yet again, and set off. Within yards at the Town Hall corner, I stopped pedalling to adjust my position on the seat. Bloody near threw myself off, it was fixed wheel, and NO three speed. Before I got anywhere near the Windmill, I was lathered in sweat and my back side was getting sore already. It was one of those thin racing seats that tries to split your bum in two.

What a journey, it was almost as bad as the night I had biked back to Cranwell in a gale. No rain this time, but a stiff East wind right in my face. On the Cranwell trip I had my three speed, of course the wind was then much worse, and it poured with rain. On occasions I had stood on the pedals in bottom gear to stay still. Today I just had to work at it, damned hard. The laugh is, we seldom get an East wind here, just when I go East on a bike.

Two and half sweaty dishevelled hours later, I took the bike from under my backside, no way could I have go my leg over the seat. Back ache from bending over the low bars. leg ache from all the work they had done, and an almost split backside. I leaned the bike against the showroom window, and walked in looking like a cripple with gout.

"Good morrow to you sir." The smell of aftershave arrived before he did. "The other gentleman is needing to pressure his lady, they will be in later, she does not want to ride in a van." (Three cheers for silly women.) The salesmen led the way into the showroom, there it was, all pristine, with a man's backside sticking out of the driver's door. My heart almost stopped.

"What's the price on this?" The man's voice questioned. Eric!!!!" He turned, ignored me and addressed the salesman again with raised eyebrows. I managed to get the hint, and kept quiet.

"Th. th. this gentleman has just come to buy it," Pongy flustered.

"No matter, what is the price?"

He quoted the price offered to me.

"Over fifty above top book." Eric pointed out.

"Yes, well, it's an above top book motor."

"Tank full of petrol, mud flaps, any tax still on it?" Eyebrows raised in sardonic question. "Oh yes, any warranty?"

All we got from 'him', was "I, um, er."

Eric chipped in. "Is Tom about?" almost casual.

"No, I'm afraid not. Mr Tom is in the South of France for two weeks."

"Pity, I will call and see him later then. Oh hullo Mr Chapman, I did not realise it was you, are you interested?"

I could only nod, speechless I guess.

"Well if you're interested I will stand back, you have done me so many favours over the years it would be silly us both keeping the price up, but do insist on some warranty, any tax still applicable, a tank full of juice, and these do really need mud flaps. I will leave you to it, I must go and see the stores and office." He turned to go.

"D.D. Do you know Mr Tom?" the sales chappie was almost to frightened to ask.

"Yes, we were at school together." With a nonchalant wave he set off, office and stores bound.

With great good fortune the garage was agent for my insurance company, and could give me a cover note to save phoning my own agent. I drove from the showroom, grinning like an idiot. Eric met me by the pumps and motioned me to stop, a smiling pensioner filled the tank, Eric put a large 'Jiffy' bag in the passenger's foot well, wished me luck and parted with. "Nice to see you again Mr Chapman, I do hope we meet again soon." Sauntered to his car and drove off.

The salesman shook my hand warmly, said he hoped to see me again soon, reminded me how reasonable their service charges were, and left me. I only just remembered to load Eric's bike in the back then drove off consumed with curiosity.

Over the level crossing and river, first left and pulled up on a large muddy layby to open the envelope. Mud flaps, a spare set of bulbs, a tax disc with almost six months left AND the petrol needle showed full!

Eric called in the morning, too busy to chat for long he had arrived yesterday on the A46 from the City, so that was why he had not passed me. He WAS at school with a lad of the same name, but doubts if it was the same person, and did have appointments today in Boston, Kings Lynn, Norwich etc, and did not expect to be home till after decent people were abed, then he was gone.

I set about giving the inside a really good clean, not that it was dirty, but underclothes and frocks can pick up muck where there is none. Began to load what was at home, then went to Mrs. Wells for the rest.

All harassed, she met me at the door. "I'm glad you've come, I've got a funny smell." Beckoning me, she went into the house as fast as the old legs would go. I followed, puzzled. At a door set in the corner, she told me to sniff. No need, it was leaking gas.

"Where is your gas main?" I asked.

"I don't have gas, I'm scared of it, my oldest son had it taken out after my husband died. We used to keep coal in the cellar, Dad always fetched it, I'm scared down there, it's dark. When they had finished doing it my son built a coal bunker in the garden and sealed the cellar for me."

I took a closer look at the door, he had, a hasp lock, a sneck, bolts top and bottom, all looked as though they had been there forever. "Have you got the key for this lock?"

She just stood and looked bewildered.

"The key, Mrs. Wells."

"I'm not going down there."

"No need to, I will."

She was going to pieces, fast. She was ringing her hands in her pinny, but had not realised she had also got a handful of her dress. I unwound it all from her fingers, just as the dress was high enough to see the bottom of her below knee length bloomer legs. What a relief, the first thing I had put in the new van was my tool bag. I sat her down in 'her' chair, told her not to bother, and went out. Her neighbour was in the garden. I asked her to phone the Gas Co. and report a gas leak, gave her a handful of change, and rushed back in with my tool bag.

The hasp lock gave little trouble, two or three sharp taps in the right place with a hammer opened that, but ALL the bolts were rusted solid. Oil, screwdriver, hammer took their time and effort. Then the neighbour came in to say Mrs. Wells did not have any gas, the gas man said so. Some fruity comments from me as I struggled with the bolts, the last one gave in, complete with torch I plunged down the steep brick steps. I guessed right first time, the gas main and meter were on the street side wall. I needed to come back for my hammer to force the gas tap over to OFF. Struggled back upstairs. The next door lady already had a cigarette in her mouth and the match out of the box ready. I shouted "NO," and knocked them to the floor. "Open every door and window," I instructed.

"But it's cold."

"I dunna care if it's snowing, open all doors and windows." I then asked where the nearest phone box was.

"I don't know."

"But I asked you to phone."

"I did."

"Where?"

"Across the road at Mrs Vincent's."

"Show me."

I shot across the road to Mrs Vincent, apologised, explained, she pointed to the phone. I will not dwell on the next fifteen minutes. The silly bugger at the other end insisted that Mrs Wells did not have gas, or a meter, all had been removed and sealed many years ago. The outcome was that they would send a gas man, but if no meter I would be charged for the man's time and transport. I told him if there WAS a meter I would charge them for MY time and transport.

"But you can't do that, it's all down in our rules and regulations."

Within ten minutes a large van arrived, not A gas man. FOUR of the buggers. Led by a little fat pompous ass in a navy suit and bowler hat. Very red face, and very full of his own importance.

"I must warn you again Mr Wells that IF there is no meter you will be charged labour and transport."

"Is that why you brought all the troops to boost the bill? And the name is not Wells."

By now, poor Mrs Wells was almost in shock, she was visibly trembling. I asked the lady next door to take her home and make her a cup of tea.

257

"I will make her one here," she suggested.

"No you bloody well won't, you will take her to YOUR home."

Pompous ass of the bowler hat was still twittering about "no gas" etc. The open doors and windows having cleared the worst. I had just about had enough of him I took his ear between my finger and thumb, frog marched him down the cellar steps and put his nose on the meter. "WHAT'S THAT?"

"I.I. er. according to our records... CHARLIE!! bring the blower and the chaps down here will you?"

They used a sort of industrial vacuum cleaner on 'blow', in no time at all, all smell gone, but they left Mrs. Wells with a lot of dusting to do. The four 'slaves' and I exchanged winks a grins, but 'he' with the bowler hat and smudge of dirt on his nose end never spoke to me again.

I only brought the stock I really needed, poor Mrs. Wells had had enough for one day, I got back home feeling rung out and dirty

There were three in the yard waiting for me, ALL to look at my new acquisition. (How on earth does news travel so fast?) The first to speak was Freddie.

"That chap you sold your car to, is it a Mr Allfus from the Alley or similar?"

I admitted it was.

"He was in the pub at lunch time boasting he had been to Skeggy and back in under three and a half hours and he had included a three pint stop."

I blanched at the thought of my little car in such hands.

"That's not all. He has never passed or taken a

driving test, has no licence, and got less than thirty to the gallon, he's moaning."

Silence whilst my mind absorbed this information.

"You did give a receipt and keep a copy?"

"Yes, plus a comment to the effect I had warned him about insurance laws."

"That's alright then, he can get up to all the daft tricks he likes, you should be in the clear." He went on his way.

My old Smeeton pal had been standing by, awaiting his chance, he would never ever barge in.

"Yes I do like it, you have done right, it will serve you well, now stop drooling and listen to me, Dad's latest. He had to go to Birmingham the day before yesterday, his only transport is his big old four and a half litre Sunbeam. In the middle of all that mess you know so well, he stalled it at traffic lights, when he tried to restart, the starter dog jammed in the flywheel ring gear. It does happen on occasions. One helluva job to free it. He sat, lit his pipe, and thought, chap behind in a hurry, so he blew his horn, Dad got the pipe going really well before he got out and walked back.

"Would you do me a big favour?"

Caught on the hop, the chap asked "What?"

"Will you please go and start my car for me, while I stop here and blow your horn for you?"

I can well imagine the fellow was not amused.

"Dad tried to explain, it was a major job, no way could he push over two tons of motor car. What did the man suggest?"

The chappie uttered some profane words reversed,

and crept round Dad's waggon, Dad mused. "He had been a member of the R.A.C. for well over thirty years and had never ever called on them. Now is the time. He left a gaggle of people grunting and pushing whilst he went to find a phone box. He explained to me, in his usual pain staking way, all this, saying "do you know within twenty minutes, a big black man from Jamaica arrived in an R.A.C. van. I think that's very good going in the middle of Birmingham."

My brother's voice from the background. "From Jamaica I reckon that is BLOODY GOOD GOING."

Another mate awaiting in the wings so to speak, he was a wage clerk at the local colliery, bubbling as usual, he also looked the van over, made the right sort of noises, then came out with the REAL reason he had called. Since the war we had an influx of all sorts from Yorkshire, Wales, Staffs, Scotland, Estonia, Poland, etc drafted into the pits. One black man they could never find in the dark. When they were off, too ill to collect their wages, it was accepted that they send their nearest and dearest with a note for wage collection. One such from a Pole who had married an English girl.

"Dear, I have a boil in my groin, and unable to fetch myself, would you please see to my wife. Hopping this meets with your approval. Clementine Lesnavitch."

Chuckling. I carried on loading until dark.

It was almost two weeks before I saw Eric again, he did not look at all well, his face was pinched and drawn, his complexion sallow.

"What on earth is wrong with you?" I questioned.

"I'm having a rough time, nothing is going right at

all. The last time I saw you I had a full day booked. I made six appointments, East Coast down to Boston, then Kings Lynn, on to Norwich. Had all the times fixed perfect for doing consultations on the return trip. Not a single bloody sale. One old dear in Lincolnshire did not feel very well, she asked if I could go somewhere else first and call back. The next call was twenty miles away, it was the young son doing a project on hearing, all he wanted was to ask questions and scrounge literature. By the time I got back to the old dear she had died. Bad luck in a way, but had I been testing when she died it would have been much more difficult. At least I could tell the boss she did not want to buy and made it obvious. (He still had his distorted humour) The last call was very late on, he lived on the top floor in a high rise flat. The lift did not work when I made the appointment in the morning, it still did not work. I carried all my heavy gear up all those stairs, he was not in. Forgotten or chickened out? Similar luck ever since. I've advised three with a low tone hearing loss to consider surgery, the boss does not like that, no profit." Eric literally subsided on to his car mudguard and tried to light a cigarette. I held his hand to steady the trembling flame of his lighter. Then he almost gasped with his first lung full of smoke. "Almost three weeks without a single sale."

We were both silent for ages, what could I say or do? Naturally I felt for him, but that was of no help.

Eventually, with a wan half smile, he shook himself like a dog. "When the going gets tough, the tough get going. What have you done to impress Barrie Vincent?"

"Nothing. I've not seen him for months."

"You have, he's most impressed."

"I do see his wife every week."

"So, you're making his wife?"

"Don't be silly, she is such a nice person, a good friend, I would do nothing to spoil our relationship."

His old quizzical grin returned with a questioning look.

"That is not funny." I was hurt by his implications.

"Well, what have you sold her then?"

"I delivered an English Electric 4002 R washer a couple of weeks ago."

"Where did you leave it?"

"By her back door, she was washing the kitchen floor and said Barrie would bring it in."

"That's it, you carried it, dumped it, he could not pick it up. He's a rough tough collier, your a wimp of a credit draper."

"Don't be daft, look how Dad picked my car up. After a broken back, crushed foot etc. etc.

"He was one of the old school, pick and shovel brigade, Barrie will be one of the press button colliers now. Think back how we battled with Dennis gear boxes, Brad's Dodge chassis etc."

My eyes must have clouded over, thinking about Brad's Dodge, what a job. Brad was a local haulage contractor. Early in the war he was ferrying huge loads of stone to build airfield runways. He had put boards on the front, back and sides to carry more stone, a long wheel base tipper, the chassis was not up to it and kept cracking. Arthur suggested we shorten the chassis and strengthen it. What a job. We cut the chassis in two, and fixed two heavy girders inside the chassis 'H' section, then needed to rivet and bolt all together. We had to take the girders out to heavy duty drill, then the 'interesting' part to get it all lined up again. We were within 'half a hole' of true. Me with my finger in the hole to 'feel', whilst Arthur belted it from the back with a fourteen pound sledge hammer. Six or seven hefty belts produced no movement.

"Harder," I called out. He did, and the girder moved almost half an inch, my finger trapped in the hole. Banging from the back, all the room in the world, to move it back, from the front, NO room at all. All were struggling with taper punches, chisels, small pinch bars, anything they could think of. Me on my haunches with finger trapped. THINK? It was almost five hours. I had to eat my sandwiches whilst trapped, and silly me had two 'lids' of tea.!!!

Eric came to life and roared with laughter at the memory, "We all had to gather round while you peed in an oil tin, so that Miss Summer in the office would not see."

"She was quite happy with all after a swim the next Sunday morning," I smirked, yes, Miss Summers had been a real goer.

Chapter 25
Nostalgia Is So Old Fashioned

At long last, we managed to arrange a 'get together' with the old crowd. The idea was good, but the execution was a real disappointment. George had died in Egypt. Two had lost the fight for life in Jap P.O.W. camps, three aircrew lost over Germany, three more killed on the second front, one had died in a training accident in South Africa, one terminally ill, others had moved away. It all started with a sense of loss. It is only at such times that you realise just how many were no longer with us.

Len Till's cheery nature helped. He reminded me of the time when the two of us were sent out to collect and make good a pre war Humber. The Farmer owner had put it up on bricks at the start of the war. He had bought a little Ford eight for petrol economy. The winter snow of (think) 1942 caught him out. He had flipped it through a hedge and wrote it off. Cars no longer available, he needed the Humber again. On bricks since 1939, and never touched. (Will they never learn?) All tyres very flat, battery very flat, brakes and steering seized solid. We pumped for ages with a hand pump, back at base we had a compressor and an air line, but the air line was feet long, not miles.

Lifted the car off the bricks with the wrecker crane, then thought seriously. I had been a legitimate driver for at least six months. Len, not so. Would he be better towing, or being towed? In view of all the problems with the car, I decided that the 'experienced'? (Ha Ha) driver should be towed.

Found the longest rope available, warned him about no brakes, difficult steering, no electrics, take your time etc., and we set off.

My shouted instructions as he moved off. "Remember, I canna steer or stop." All was reasonable till we turned into Westgate, Market Day! A chap on two sticks appeared from behind a market stall, held one stick out to indicate he had all intentions of crossing the road, and set off. Len sounded his horn, flashed his lights and waved out of the cab window. Relief, he saw and waited, but after Len in the wrecker had passed, he looked after him, swearing at his bad manners and carried on walking. Me, arriving on the end of a long rope, no brakes, no lights, no horn, and very little steering. I did miss him, just, and left him gesturing, and swearing, still not realising the mess we were in, or how lucky he had been.

The same winter we had heavy snow early on, the traffic rutted it, then the heavy frost arrived, froze all the ruts solid. Three days later, an even heavier snow fall covered all the ruts. It was sheer hell getting to work on the bike. If I guessed right and kept between the ruts, no problem, but hit a rut of ice, and over the top I went. Needless to say, I arrived at work covered in bruises and late.

They needed me, the Wrecker was tanked up ready and waiting. "A Morris Ten in a ditch in Derbyshire. "You will manage on your own won't you.?"

It took simply ages to find. (Remember, no sign posts) And as a matter of interest I have never ever found that place again.

I drove slowly up a small hump back bridge, there

was the Morris, about twenty feet off the road, all four wheels in what had been a ditch, but was now a small river. I pipped my horn to let him know I had arrived, put the brakes on, and slid into the river behind him!

Morris owner was not impressed at all, but I was seventeen and unflappable.

"I will soon have us both out." In boots, calf deep running water, with just a shovel???? Before I got the wrecker out, another car had joined us, before I got the Morris out, two more had joined the party. By dusk, I was tired out, cold, and wet through, I was just dragging the last one out, when a white van arrived on top of the little bridge, it had red flashes all over it, and the words 'Bolsover Colliery Company' painted on the doors. He put his brakes on and sailed straight in to join us. I had at that stage never ever seen a man so scared before. He was trembling with fear.

"You're alright," I assured him. "You will soon be out, I've been at this all day."

"B.B.Bu but the van's loaded with dynamite."

"That's alright, it needs detonating."

"Th Th The detonators are in as well, the other van wouldn't start."

A few moments silence, then Eric spoke. "You know youth, we ought to write a book."

"But who would believe any of it?"

He was smiling again, and looking thoughtful. Not always a good sign. "I did tell you about that little red haired lad, he had only just started walking. He shambled ahead of me, climbed up on to a gate and looked back all knowing, before commenting. "By gum Mester, them

266

beauns is looking well."

"He sounds to be a great little character."

"He's worse now, my last sale was to his Gran. It's his fifth birthday any time. Gran was telling me they all were dressing up to go to his Auntie's wedding."

"What's a wedding Gran?"

"She explained that when he grew up he would meet and fall in love with a lady, whom he would then marry and go away to live with her."

He burst into tears. "He did not want to live with anyone but his Mam."

Panic over, Mum busied herself putting lipstick on.

"What's that for?"

"To make me beautiful."

He just sat, looked at her intently for ages, she had to ask. "Why was he looking?"

"How long before it begins to work?"

After all the wedding panic was over Mum was discussing with him that soon, he would be going to school.

"It's no good me going."

"Why not?"

"I can't read or write."

I could tell by Eric's body language, he really liked that little character. His face softened as he finished off. "As I was leaving, he went rushing past, being towed by a large Lurcher dog, poor little chap's feet were hardly touching the floor. 'Are you taking Doggy a walk?' I called after him."

His face, flushed almost to the colour of his hair turned to shout back.

"No, I'm taking him where he wants to go."

Lurcher, that reminded me about Sam Shutt, he used to breed them. "I saw Sam Shutt last week, he asked to be remembered to you." Eric then really laughed.

"Does he still run his Lancaster? I was always extracting his urine about it, asking how many gallons it did to the mile etc. I have even written the name down for him, Lanchester, not Lancaster, but he never ever realised. Then his brother in law with his 'Towering Coupe', it was a Riley touring coupe."

Len chipped in, wasn't it him whose Father died from prostrate? We had to laugh, sad though it was. I used to say "He's prostrate now even if it was prostate problems."

"Remember my driving lessons? I used to scare the pants off both of you." That raised a torrent of abuse from both seniors.

One day, he would only be fourteen at the time, we had to go up to Greenwoods joiner's yard. The yard gates were big and heavy, needed the two of us to get them open. Len had shot back into the driving seat saying. "I can drive it to the yard can't I?"

Smiling at his cheek, I had agreed and sat on the mudguard. "You had decided to show your skill at driving without using the clutch. You must have been doing fifty, and I only had the wing mirror to hang on to, I expected to be thrown off when you braked."

The cherubic grin lighting up his face Len smiled. "Fifty five, but who's counting, I thought you were going to have a lavatorial accident. Then Clive had arrived, poor Clive, we all treated him rotten, po faced, always so serious, we sent him for rubber hammers, sheets of paint, the lot The Ford foreman called him thrombosis, till he had looked it up in the dictionary. (Bloody Clot)

"Any knowledge on Alexandre Street?" I asked Eric.

"Yes, keep away," he advised, then laughed. "I never did get the money, but we all got a good laugh. A poor call, for weeks I knocked on the back door, they all fled out of the front, then I got wise. I knocked on the back, then galloped to the front and let myself in. There they all were, caught in full flight, but! the front floorboards were rotten, when I jumped in the boards gave way and I stood with scuffed shins, one leg each side of a joist. The next morning I saw his Missus at the Coop, she bought a Soda Siphon on the book, took it outside, squirted it all down the drain, then took the empty siphon back in for the deposit money. Needed it to go to Bingo."

"Had a cracker in the next street though as straight as a die, but really obnoxious, the son in particular. They were factory plumbers, Dad and son had a van each, all fitted and tooled out. The son had fitted his with drop down beds, a Calor Cooker etc. His delight was the Lakes or Scotland. He would drive up any road marked as unsuitable for motors, go as far as he could get, then camp for the night. I will do my best to tell the yarn in his words."

"T' weather were real smashing youth, drove rate ter top a this 'ill and camped. Looking straight dern this big lake. It were that light I could still read at midnight. Next mornin' we drove back dern, right at t' bottom were an 'ump bridge. I were comin' up it an 'ad ter stop, big 'umber coming. Me 'umour were good, so I dropped her in reverse, then realised tuther bloke 'expected' me to back off. No bloody way I thought, and chucked it back inter neutral. We just sat theer and luked at each other. Then 'ee gets a cigar out and lit it, so I lit a Woodbine. His Missus gives 'im the paper and ee starts ter read. I asked Heather for me buke. Then 'is Missis gets t' flask ert and pours 'im a coffee. I opens t' winder so's ee could 'ere, ses to are Heather, light gas and put t' kettle on and drop t' bunks were in fer a long wait. 'ee backs off at that."

Chapter 26
Is This What They Call Success?

Years do roll by, almost unnoticed, I suppose things were going pretty well, and yet Eric's words were ringing so true. I was working longer hours, had a much bigger book debt, BUT! at the end of each week I could not afford to take more out, it was all in the customers' homes. The youngsters got married, Mum and Dad had traded with me, so they did, and were good ten bob or pound a week regular customers. But Mum and Dad had bought clothing, sheets, rugs, the youngsters wanted Fridges, washers, three piece suites, fitted carpets, and clothes as well. (For the same payment). I tried diplomacy, talking like a Dutch uncle, then in some cases got to be rude. They bought elsewhere, and began to miss me to pay them. It was all seeming to me as a 'no win' situation. Eric had also tried a fresh route, the London firm did not like him being quite so fair. Derek had admired his honesty, but pointed out that they did not make profit by being so scrupulous.

Eric had replied. "I treat them as I would wish to be treated." So, Eric had left, and started on his own yet again. So far he had his head above water if only just. His wife was really of little help, she could spend money, she did earn herself, but she could spend hers AND his. Hair done every week, posh new clothes with astounding regularity, the large garden, high hedges all round took a lot of time and effort. "I want my privacy." But it was Eric teetering on the top step to trim the eight foot high hedges with double decker buses within inches that was doing the struggling.

Meals, she arrived from work at five twenty, put him steak, brussels, and tatties in the pressure cooker for twenty minutes, then put it on a plate, under the grill, till he arrived home at sometimes eleven o'clock at night. He almost burst into tears one night telling me.

"Y'know, I've never ever had a fresh cooked meal in all my life. Dad got home from pit about three, me from School at four, from the garage at six thirty. But Mum did put it on a steamer, not under the bloody grill." The Missus also insisted that their bed be shared by two large dogs. "They only need a cuddle," but there they were fast asleep on the bed every morning.

He had asked my advice after admitting he had been 'seeing?' the daughter of a local tradesman.

"It's no good asking me, I've problems of my own I can't sort," I admitted. "You were so right about the book debt, it's really sky high."

With a worried grin, he just advised. "Don't let anyone talk you into an overdraft, it gets even worse." With a half hearted wave, he turned and went, leaving me deep in thought. The bank manager had been pestering for weeks now.

I called round to see Mum and Dad. For years now I had pleaded with him to keep the little bitch on a lead when she was in season. Not a hope, on top of which every night he took a different walk route, letting the dogs from every direction know.

"There's no cain fer yer ter worry, no dog will get near 'er." Tapping a pocket full of large stones and brandishing his walking stick. But one had!!!!

As far as I could make out he had kicked the two dogs apart, then thrashed the other dog owner for letting it get so near. But, the damage had been done. Her teats grew, her body swelled, all he did was sit with her on his knee, stroking, murmuring "Poor little duck."

I suggested she should see the Vet. "Weer's munney comin' from fer Vet's bills?"

No doubt, she was ill, I risked all the wrath and took her. I held her head whilst the Vet probed up her backside. "Poor dog, her nose is really warm," I informed Rodger the Vet.

"So would yours be if I had my hand up your backside." With a serious shake of his head Rodger came out with his opinion. "I fear we are too late, she has at least four pups dead in her womb. I will take them away now, and hope, but the outcome is very dodgy."

It was well after midnight when a tired subdued Vet came out into the yard to me. I was chain smoking in the van.

"There's nothing either of us can do now, she'd got five, all putrefied, be best if you go home and ring in the morning."

I had to agree, even though I realised I was for it when I reported to Dad. I did so as quick as I could and came out, went home, to bed but no real sleep.

"Rodger phoned me just before eight in the morning, she had just died. I had to go and report to parents before I dare start work. Of course, Dad ranted, raved, swore, on occasions he tore round the house like a demented being, all guilt really, it was his fault. I shot off to the town to pay Rodger and thank him for trying.

Dad now hated me, it was all my fault?? He never spoke, so I limited my calls to Mum when I guessed he would be out. It worked well for some weeks, till one day in he walked in whilst I was still visiting. ALL SMILES???

"Charlie, frum 't pit 'as a Jack Russell in pup, they are due next wik." I stormed out fuming, Mum followed. "He's not fit to have a dog," I mouthed at her.

She spoke back the same way. "You should know him by now."

He was now hardly ever at home, constantly visiting the new litter. It appears that he had picked the one he wanted the day they were born. A little bitch again, the last, smallest runt. Then he began to borrow it, bringing it home in his pocket, nursed it for a few hours before taking it back. All and sundry told him he was wrong to do so, all were ignored. Then he wanted to keep it, at five weeks? No way was it sense, but he must have pestered till Charlie gave in. Under six weeks old, he even tried to take the poor little mite a walk.

All my life I could remember Dad as useless, he worked hard, earned money, did the garden, nothing else. No matter what needed attention in the house, we had the cry. "T' man at pit ses." Car faults, decorating, Doctor, Vet, door catches, gate hinges, fuses. "T' man at pit ses."

After all, Charlie was a "Man at t' pit", but with the pup, it was no good what he said.

However, all things have their lighter moments. He nursed the pup constantly, between them they had invented a game, Dad would lean forward and 'nuzzle' it. Moving his head back just before the little teeth or paws

274

could protest. Such was the situation one night when Eric called with me. None of us had realised, the pup was growing, its reactions were improving. Mum, Eric, and I were sat at the table with a pot of tea. Down went Dad's head, up came the pup's teeth to meet it. Two needle sharp eye teeth caught hold of the bit of flesh between his nostrils, he jerked his head back, the pup held on. He tried to take its weight in his hands, it wriggled free, all it's weight hanging on his nose, blood all over the place, air blue. He sort of tore it away and hurled it to the floor, it scampered up on Mum's knee. He rushed to the kitchen tap, Eric and I rushed out before we lost control. Signing to each other, "What do we do?" Neither of us dare or could speak. I motioned to the car, we got in and fled. At the top of the lane I had to stop, we were both crying with laughter.

"Your, your Mam, will she be alright?" Eric eventually gasped.

"I do hope so, but I dare not go back."

Even the incontinent clouds on our journey home could not damp our humour. We DID call at the Hare, we DID think we deserved one, and Eric DID keep it going on his mother in law.

"I've told you how thick she is?" I just nodded through tears.

"One of my school mates was on Air Crew training in South Africa, he stayed on after the war in the South African army, a Major would you believe? He called to see us, she was drinking tea. I introduced him as my friend from Africa. All bright she said that she had thought all Africans were black."

"Oh no ses he. The officers are white, but we have black privates."

"I shall never ever forget the look on her face."

Chapter 27
A Good Christmas

Another reason I was short, 'she' had talked me into putting a deposit down on a little bungalow, nothing pretentious, but in the long term??? Better than paying rent.

One major problem it did save was who to go where and when for Christmas. All parents could now come to us, with delight I invited all four parents for Christmas Day.

All seemed happy apart from 'Her' Mum. "What about Auntie Millie, Now she has lost George she's on her own. So I phoned Auntie Millie.

"Yes, she would love to come, but what about spinster cousin Doris, who had always spent Christmas with them?"

The fact that Aunty Millie lived in Pontefract and Doris lived the 'other' side of Nottingham was not noticed. (Only by me) 'Her' parents five miles away, 'thataway', my parents five miles 't'uther' way. I could not see 'any', perched on the Bedford wood slatted seats at the back, it would mean four separate journeys.

Christmas Eve I bought a dozen bottles of beer and a bottle of sherry. Eight o' clock Christmas morning I set off for Pontefract, by ten thirty I had Aunt Millie ensconced with Sherry bottle and set off for Nottingham. By twelve I had Aunt and cousin around the Sherry, and then fetched 'her' parents, whilst they joined the throng I went for mine. No one was more surprised than I to have everyone seated by minutes after one o'clock.

'Her' Dad had seen away four pint bottles, the sherry was not looking at all well, in spite of which, Doris had almost knitted a jumper. I put a bottle by the side of my Dad's plate, and he spent all the meal time 'twirling' it and reading everything printed thereon.

The little pup was now almost six months old, very pretty, very sharp, with very appealing eyes. "PLEASE do not give her any food," I asked. Everybody did, so just as soon as we had cleared the table she was sick in the middle of the new carpet.

Her Dad liked to watch T.V., my Dad liked a nap, Aunt Millie was into politics, Doris was into knitting and organising everyone. (Ex School teacher) Her Mum liked to natter and my Mum was bewildered by it all.

I had been parading the dog round the yard whilst Jane cleared her mess, and the other two ladies washed up. We all returned to the room for an easy afternoon. Poor Mum, we sat her in an easy chair with her back to the French window. (less chance of her sticky out legs tripping anyone) The dog set off towards Mum's knee. Then she spotted her reflection in the window. Tail up, she advanced trying to growl. BUT! her reflection advanced, so she whimpered and hid behind Mum's chair. Peeped out, other dog gone, all brave again, she went to look for it. It was coming her way again. This pantomime must have gone on for half an hour, all humans were helpless, I drew the curtains, but she still had an occasional peep to make sure we were safe. In my opinion, the high light of the day.

About ten p.m., thinking about the mileage involved I suggested it was going home time. Cousin Doris insisted on being first, she had so much to do on the morrow??? (Living on her own?)

It must have been freezing for hours, the roads were like glass. The 'White Post' hill was littered with cars struggling. I used second, with a bit of 'slipping clutch' I managed to weave through the ruck. Doris, oblivious, still knitting in the dark.

Needless to say, the conditions slowed down my time table somewhat, it was after two a.m. when I flopped into an easy chair by the fire. In the hearth was one bottle of beer, very warm. I was trying to enjoy it when I saw coins in the fireplace. One and nine pence, Dad had paid for his beer.

After all, Christmas is a time to enjoy yourself.

Chapter 28
Chaos

Eric called at something after ten in the morning. "Would I mind helping him to take his dog a walk... ????

Still full of yesterday and the pup I was trying to fill him in. Eric did not hear, care, show interest, or appreciate.

"What's up youth?"

"I've told the Missis I'm leaving her."

"I can't see any bruises."

"There aren't any, I would feel better if there were." A big, big sigh.

"I dropped what I thought would be my bombshell. Her answers."

"Why don't you have an affair and keep it quiet." Then, "Why don't you go to someone nice like Barbara?" Followed by "Will you wait till after Mother has died," then pleaded for a month for time to tell her Mother."

"This morning I have met a customer who already knew."

We must have walked over a mile without even exchanging a glance, I had to speak. "Do you think she just wanted you as a figure head?"

"I don't know what to think, before, I had doubts of what I was doing, after that reaction, I have none at all."

I hardly said another word, he had occasional bouts of swearing as his mind recalled what he called 'instances'.

"I should have realised, the very first night in our own bed. I had a pee, opened the window and got into bed. She had a pee, closed the window and got into bed. We had a sort of 'leg over', I peed again, opened the window and got into bed. She got out, peed, closed the window and got back in."

"I would have put my foot through it and said right, now shut that bugger."

"You who promised everyone that you would never ever get to be like your Dad." He was laughing, I shut up.

"We all know your Dad, mine was almost as bad, my idea of wedding bells was not the rows and temper we have both suffered. IF there are children, would you want 'yours' to have the life we had?"

I turned to him, put a hand on each shoulder, looked him straight in the eye, and spoke what I thought was wisdom. "I suggest we discuss this another time, our brains are not clear, we will give ourselves a few days thinking time." He put his arms around my shoulders and sobbed his socks off.

We eventually meandered, no one could have called it walked, till almost fully recovered, we arrived at 'the seat', yes, the one on Churm's Lane yet again I nodded towards it. "Fag time?" He agreed, we sat and lit up.

He looked and sounded to be normal by the time Dot England's little Sheltie appeared, closely followed by the lady herself. "This the seat of all confessions?" as she joined us. Then whispered in my ear. "Hubby's werks are werking again." She looked radiant, no, she positively glowed. Possibly sensing we were not receptive, I suppose we were un naturally quiet. She leered at us. "Hubby will be home in minutes, must rush home and make him a coffee, I promised." With a suggestive wink at me she was gone.

Eric and I separated, I asked him to call if he needed, wait if he didn't. I got home and was surprised to find Mae, in her boy friends car, waiting in the street.

"Who's a big girl and driving now?" I grinned at her.

"Dad wanted you to teach me, we had rows. I dare not tell why it had better not be you, you'd be on your knees by now."

"Serious now Uncle Ron, your the only one I can ask and get a straight answer. Can a woman help herself?"

I just looked puzzled.

She tried again, blushing. "Y'know instead of the man doing it himself can she help herself?"

I grinned, "Not without him knowing, that's for sure."

She looked so relieved, "I didn't think so, but one of my friends said that she once did." She leaned over, kissed me, and drove off with a happy wave.

Chapter 29
Holiday?

Last year we had taken the tent to Scotland. TWO WHOLE weeks off!

It had rained all of every bloody day. My intentions were to travel back from Gairloch in two days, Friday, camp up for the night. Saturday home, leaving Sunday to prepare for work. Friday it rained harder than ever, I delayed for a day. Saturday just as bad, dare not delay further. I strapped the soggy tent on top of the chariot with bungy cord and set off. What a journey. Coming through the top of Glen Coe the water squirted from the cliff side like a car wash, I just had to give way and stop for a nap behind the wheel somewhere near the border. I've always hated being stuck behind a caravan, but after a journey like that I had to reconsider. I bought myself a little one.

The wife and I considered and discussed. 'If I rush round Friday night, then do any dodgy Saturday calls the day early, we can get away early Saturday morning, we could come back home on Monday Eve.'

It was all planned for the weekend after next, so this weekend was a flurry of preparation. Saturday night I serviced and washed the van, Sunday I started on the filthy caravan, It had stood, unused, for months. Covered in mud and green algae. The first job was to scrub what I could off with a hose brush, leathered it dry, then started to scrub with the latest cleaner polish that I had seen advertised. I started on the roof, working at full stretch from a ladder, followed by the rear and the two sides.

Silly to leave the worst till last, but, I had, the front was caked with dead flies etc as well as mud with some cow pats. The arms were already beginning to ache, but now the REAL pain arrived. Upper arms and chest, I was in agony. I had seen so many customers shrug off such pains as 'nothing', only to be buried within days. I asked my lady to ring the Doctor.

He arrived within half an hour, he 'thought' it 'might' be a heart attack?? Then left three pills to take when the pain got too bad. If no improvement ring him in the morning. None, so we phoned, he was with me in what seemed to be minutes. A quick check over, he asked to borrow the phone and rang for the ambulance. Just as soon as he had left us, the pain went! So I had a bath and shave. I had only just finished when the blood wagon arrived. I said I felt alright. They ignored me, strapped me into a little chair and carried me out. Peering through the dark glass en route I asked where we were going. They told me. I re routed them and saved over a mile. The sarcastic driver suggested I apply for a job as ambulance driver.

They carried me in on my little chair, wished me well, and departed. A nurse arrived with a clip board and a sheet of questions a mile long. Within half an hour she knew all about me apart from that I smoked and how often I got my 'legover'.

The sister then arrived, identical form, we went through it all again. I was put to bed. Within ten minutes the house Doctor arrived, same form, same questions. Then the specialist arrived and went through it all again. I could stand no more. I was going to suggest they bought a copier, but instead questioned. "I thought smoking was a heart No No?"

"It is."

"Well why don't you ask?"

"We are not sure."

They wired me for sound, put a little 'press it if you want us button' in my hand, and left me alone. I fell asleep. A gentle shake woke me. Dracula had come for blood. She stuck a plastic contraption in the back of my hand, plus about three punctures for more of my life liquid. The next time she came for more, I wrote 'Dracula' on her little box in red nail varnish I had found in my locker.

At ten p.m. they woke me again to ask if I wanted a sleeping pill. I shrugged them off, and dropped off again. At something after midnight a terrible screaming woke me. A new chap in the bed opposite appeared to be in agony. I was bursting for a pee, so pressed my little button for my own relief as well as for the other chap. Nothing happened. Ten minutes passed, I pressed it again, still nothing. Twenty minutes later I was in dire need, the chap opposite was frantic. I disconnected all my little patches. It was still some minutes before anything happened, then all hell broke loose. Bodies arrived at speed from all directions. I said what, and why I had done. They scolded me, but at least I had a urine bottle, and the chap opposite was getting attention.

Some time later, the chap was still in agony, the Specialist was with him. "Would he like a Paracetomol?"

"Anything, but please stop this bloody pain." A nurse drew his screens, and all was lost to view. I am normally a very heavy sleeper, but the rest of the night was to say the least, fitful. Noise, screams, scuffles, then silence. They nudged me awake in the morning, the bed opposite was empty.

"Where's matey?" I asked, nodding across.

"We've moved him," I was told. I later learned they had, to the mortuary!

Eggs, full fat milk, chips, sausages, beef burgers were offered. I queried the sense of all that fat. "We are not really sure."

"So if we all die it must be right, if we all live, it's not so?" They left me.

I had not been to the toilet. "Can I go?"

"No, your bed fast, heart attack. Do you want a bed pan?"

No point, no desire, I only wanted to try.

I must have missed lunch, it was almost tea time when I next surfaced. "Have you seen the specialist?" the voice from the next bed asked.

I looked blank.

"He's been round, probably would not wake a sleeping dog. He said I can't drive for six months."

I was just about to make sympathetic noises, when realisation of possibilities hit me. Tea came, I pushed it around the plate without interest, a very worried man.

The specialist returned, I beckoned him over. "The chap next door says he can't drive for six months."

"That's right, the same applies to you."

I almost hit the roof. "That's me finished, kaput, end of road, put me down now."

He almost laughed, he put a friendly hand on my

shoulder. "It's not that bad, it's only six months."

I shrugged his hand away and almost screamed at him, "No income for six months, I have monthly bills to pay, every penny I get I have to collect. I haven't any capital, living hand to mouth as it is."

He smiled and said. "We have a D.H.S.S. man come every other day, I will see that he sees you."

That did it, I blew. "I'm self employed, all the bloody D.H.S.S. do for me is take money off me."

"Well I'll send the almoner then."

"You can send Ali who the bloody hell you like it will not do me any good."

"Keep calm, all will be well, I'll see if he can come tomorrow."

By now I was sobbing with frustration, the horror, the fear, this was the bitter end. The man went with a look of resignation.

Within minutes the sister arrived, syringe poised ready.

"Is that to put me down?"

"No, just to calm you down."

"Well stuff it up his arse then," I nodded to the big man's retreating back. "He does need it." I slumped down on the bed, covered myself with the blanket. No hope, no light, not even a bloody tunnel.

The next day they came with a wheel chair, disconnected all my electrics, put me in the wheel chair to go for X Ray. We must have passed twelve toilets en route, at each and every one I pleaded to be let in to 'try'.

"Why not?"

"You're bed fast, we would have to take your wires

off."

"The bloody wires are off, they are back in the bloody ward." All was ignored.

That night, after much moving round of beds, I found myself almost in the main ward. I had been in almost an annex, it was all dark in there, no lights at all. In came the registrar I had never ever seen a man so black. His skin almost glowed a blue black. He sauntered round, deep in thought, stethoscope at the ready, then turned to go into the darkest part of the annexe.

I pleaded with him. "Please do not go in there, we shall never ever find you again."

The man was not amused, with a glare of hatred, he fled off the ward.

In the morning, two male nurses arrived to prepare a patient for surgery. Very nice boys, they simpered and giggled at each other as they worked on the bed opposite me. Then they began to jack the bed up. From my position, I could see that the bed head was under a shelf on the wall. "Hang on a minute chaps." I called out. They waved me to shut up until they had finished, and carried on jacking. "KERASH!!!" The shelf was ripped from the wall.

After tea, two young nurses arrived and removed all my sticky patches, they said I was free to move around. "Toilet?" I questioned.

"If you like."

I went, and enjoyed contemplating my navel for almost half an hour. How very pleasant. I came out, and 'fell in' behind the curvy nurse from Rewark, whom I had threatened with all sorts whilst fast in bed.

"Now is the time," was all I said. She turned, saw me, squealed and set off at a gallop. I could keep up with her at a not too brisk walk. It was all of fifteen yards into the ward, where she collapsed out of breath in the Sister's chair. "You need to be a patient, not me, at less than a third of my age you're in terrible shape." I warned.

After breakfast next morning, I just sat on my bed and sulked. I had looked at my situation from every possible angle, I could not find a ray of hope or light. I felt that I was a doomed man. I had seen no signs of the D.H.S.S. or even Ali whoever. I knew why of course, they had nothing for me. Someone approaching, the light was behind him, he was just a silhouette. He arrived and came round the bed. 'Twas himself, the specialist, smiling.

"I have come to tell you we have decided it was not a heart attack. We suspect it may have been a chest muscle strain. You will be discharged after the Houseman has seen you tomorrow." I could have hugged him.

"What about diet?" I questioned. "I thought eggs and fat were bad. I've had full cream milk, butter, etc in here, never touch them at home."

"Well, we're not really sure."

Five whole days without a smoke, and never really 'needed'. Within what seemed like minutes going through my post at home I was half way through a packet. Income tax demand for six hundred and eighty. A supplier said he had not yet got his cheque for LAST month?? So I owed him nine hundred plus, then of course it was already current month end, with no takings at all last week. ALL turned out to be in error though,

289

after much discussing, haggling, and smoking. I had everything in line before the month was out. Twenty cigarettes a day, rushed or no meals, too much hassle, not enough sleep, and too much to drink. Life was grand again.

After three months or so, I was 'invited' ? Ha Ha. To go in to Hospital to see the head specialist for a check up.

This, is, the head man? A Doctor?? Possibly eight stone, weedy, bald, specs on the end of his nose. He did not look at all well. If I had sneezed the shock would have killed him. Without looking at me, the man questioned.

"Any pain?"

"No."

"Any exercise?"

"Yes."

"What?"

"A two mile brisk walk every morning, an hour's swim every week, and two hours geriatric badminton a week, loading and unloading the van countless times, carrying loads to and from the van." He stopped me.

"How brisk is this two mile walk?"

"I do it in twenty minutes."

"How do you know?"

"I've measured it and wear a watch."

"What is this geriatric badminton?"

"An over fifties group, some are ex county players, they all play for keeps. No quarter is given or asked for."

All this without even looking at me, and he certainly never ever touched me.

"I will discharge you, if anything happens, come

back and see me."

Curled up with laughter, I was unable to speak. His doleful eyes looked up from his sheaves of paper.

"Have I said something amusing?"

Struggling to recover, I pointed out. "If anything 'does' happen, the one sure thing is, I will NOT be coming back."

Chapter 30
It's Always The End Of The Road For Someone

Poor Mum, her pain was getting worse she could hardly move about. She wrote to the Doctor asking for more pill's, he gave the prescription to the chemist, who passed the bottle to the greengrocer next door, who delivered on his weekly rounds. She asked me to take her in. It took ages to get her in, and out of the van. Then all he did was to arrange a hospital visit, she was to wait till she heard. So I loaded her again and un loaded her back home. Her appointment eventually arrived. Would I please arrange an ambulance through the Doctor.

Of course. I made an appointment, and sat in the waiting room for over half an hour before my buzzer went.

He sat at his desk writing, without looking up. "Yes?"

"Would you please arrange an ambulance for Mum, her hospital appointment has arrived."

He looked up at me, eyes full of sheer venom. "Do you think I've nothing better to do than make bloody appointments?"

Taken aback, is the least I can offer. I fear that I sort of stuttered. "S.S.Sorry, t. tell me what I should do?"

"I'll do it now your here. " He scribbled on his jotter pad and pressed his buzzer for the next person. I retired, feeling very much at a loss.

She went in, the surgeon dislocated her hip, scraped the ball and socket free from imperfections, and put her back together again. After about ten days she was sent to a recovery unit.

Poor little soul, her now wizened little face was turning yellow, it looked pitiful against the stark white hospital pillow. In a month she was back at home. Still in pain, still limping, and still gobbling codeines as if they were smarties.

"I do wish you would not take so many pills," I remonstrated with her.

Then for the first and only time in my life I heard her swear. "I've got the bloody pain lad, not you."

Weeks later, she again asked me to see the doctor about an ambulance, the surgeon needed to check. After the last time I queried her instructions. She passed me the card. "If you are aged, infirm, or need transport, see your doctor, who will arrange an ambulance." I put the card in my pocket.

I walked in again, this time he did look up. I placed the card before his eyes, underlined the magic words with my pen, and raised my eyebrows. He scribbled on his jotter and called out "NEXT." (Whatever happened to his buzzer?)

I left, and promptly set about changing doctors for all the whole family.

The new doctor was as different again, not young for someone starting out. Balding, four children, lived in a council house, an old banger car, the look of envy on his face when he spotted Dad's four ton of coal in the coal house plus over two ton stacked at the side had me making a mental promise. If ever!

Then Charlie's wife phoned, how was I? How was the dog? Then she explained that its long legs and spotty body were caused by her Mother being mated with a smooth haired terrier. She seemed to rabbit on for ages with such inane chatter before she dropped her bombshell.

"Your Mum's in hospital. I phoned for an ambulance, it sounded to me as though she has been on the bedroom floor almost all night. Your Dad was just sitting in the kitchen, staring at the dead fire, doing nowt."

No information as to which hospital, never mind a ward number. I started at the General, lucky, I had guessed right. It took ages to find out that I was right, then more time still to get the correct ward. She was in the end bed, by the door, in a coma. I could not help the staff, the staff could not help me. I just sat for two or more frustrating hours.

Aunt Ethel and Uncle Bob arrived, before I could ask how they had found out, Ethel spoke.

"This is exactly the same bed that Aunt Polly died in." Followed by "I'm glad she's unconscious, 'cos you never know what to talk about in these places." I seem to remember making a mental note. 'If ever I do write that book, these are the sort of situation comments that must be included.'

It was over two days before she came round, sister phoned to tell me, so I took Dad in. For over an hour, they neither looked at or spoke to each other, then when it was time to go, he asked. "When are yer cummin' omm?" She just closed her eyes.

We offered Dad the use of our little spare room. He refused. So it meant calling at some time every day to make sure all was well. After over a week of such visits,

Charlie's wife stopped me in the lane.

"Me, and 'er tuther side tek 'im a dinner in every day.
He dunna eat it. Even while we are there, ee puts it dern
fer T' dog. Little dog like that can't eat all that, so she
leaves it. Then ee ses it must be rubbish cos dog dunna
eat it. I for one won't be takin' 'im any more, nor will 'er
tuther side if she's any sense. In any case, my Charlie's
now in t' 'ospital, I ant got time."

I nodded in worried understanding. Mum had always
had to give him what HE wanted, when HE wanted, or
suffer. Either milk pudding or apple pie FIRST, followed
by the meat and veg. HE wanted! I thanked her and drove
down the lane, pulled up, walked into the kitchen.

There he sat, in front of the grey cold ash long dead
fire. Half a basin full of flour on his knee, stirring it with
a wooden spoon.

"Do you know what you are doing?" I questioned.

"NO!" He snarled, and threw the basin, contents, the
lot on to the fire back. Trixie, the terrified little dog,
yelped with fear, and fled from the room.

"Get your bedding, your coming with me," I
instructed.

Dad and dog ensconced at home with a pint mug of
tea and the gas fire almost full on. I went back to Dad's
home to view the situation.

I have seen pig sties more tidy. I cleared the ashes,
laid a new fire with a couple of fire lighters hidden under
the sticks. (Mum had always put tomorrow's sticks in the
oven the night before.) Opened all the windows, then
opened her little fridge door. WHAM! the stench hit me.
Milk, cheese, tomatoes, eggs. Everything either went

down the drain or wrapped and in the bin. I buried the eggs in the garden, as I looked on them as life threatening.

I could never ever remember Mum's home not smelling of wintergreen, the place now really reeked of it. No time to dust, I just went round with the vacuum cleaner, left all the windows wide open, then rushed off to try and catch up on collecting.

It was difficult. Work, going in to see Mum, coping with Dad, it lasted for all of five days. I arrived home on the fifth day, late as usual. Dad sat in the passage, coat and cap on, his bedding in a pile beside him.

"Tek me omm," he instructed.

"It will be cold, I left the windows open, there's been no fire."

"I sed, tek me omm." So I did!

Four days later when I called to see him, again he was dressed, bedding in a pile. "Tek me to your place." The same routine, all over again.

Friday morning the hospital phoned. Mum had taken a turn for the worse. Visiting not allowed, she was not fit, but would we stay by the phone?

I stood by the phone looking out of our front window. Worry gnawing at my every sinew. Like all worries, the worst ones are the ones out of your control.

Two lamp post painters arrived, complete with a box on a hydraulic lift, they must have been on piece work, they had it all polished to a fine art. One on the knobs, one in the box. As the 'boxed one' painted, the other lifted him, that post finished they moved to the next post. No doubt, the idea was to start at the top and work downwards this time, as they left the box in the 'up' position. Too late, as they moved to the next post I saw with horror, my phone line in the way. "STOP!!" I bawled. Too late, the wire parted. I went out and really tore them off a strip.

"Ring the phone people and tell them." I all but knocked him out of the cab in my frustration. No point, I rushed across the road and borrowed their phone.

The G.P.O. people were understanding and very good, soon after lunch we were re connected.

Then the penultimate message came. "Would we all please go into hospital?" Before I could get us all in the van the phone rang again, we were too late.

It is sad to lose anyone, but Mum is THE special, we all only ever get one. My immediate reaction was guilt. She had asked to be taken to see her sister. "Yes when I have time." Can we go to the sea side some time. "Yes when I have time." All the things you were going to do for her 'one day', but I never had. Now it was too late. If only I had.

After almost a week of a very sad household. Dad's things were again in the passage. "Tek me omm." So I did.

On route I called and bought him tea, milk, sugar, butter, a medley of tinned food including such as soup, and milk puddings. All I could think of that would keep his wolf from his door.

On the lane was Charlie's wife, she was in tears, she was now a widow. Charlie had had a massive stroke. I left the two of them chatting, went on to light fires, fill the fridge, and 'cupboard' the rest. They were still talking when I drove past in a rush to try and catch up on work.

Returning through the city market square, I had to stop at traffic lights. A double decker bus pulled up opposite. Not watching the lights the driver was intent on watching a couple snogging at the end of the bus shelter. Both were wearing jeans, thick sweaters, and both had long lank greasy hair I was unsure on the sex of either. What I was sure, neither had eaten for weeks, they were making a meal of each other.

The bus driver looked across at me and mouthed. "Which is which?"

I mouthed back, "They don't know, they are finding out." I drove off, the lights had changed. The bus man was still laughing to the chagrin of traffic behind his bus.

Oh what a year, chaotic is the best word I can muster. Jane at work, so she did not have the time to cope with his eating whims. I don't think he ever realised that his desired milk puddings came from a tin, browned under the grill. His Yorkshire puddings were made by HER Mother, his pie pastry was from the supermarket.

What an effort to try and keep him clean. we soon learned the best course was to steal his under clothes whilst he was in bed, leaving him only clean ones to put on in the morning. He got through six pairs of new boots. Falling asleep in front of the fire with his feet on the hearth. Uppers perfect, soles burned through.

For the first time in ages I managed to call and see Bert and Edna. Mae had married her 'weedy one' and had moved away. Bert's boss had died. The widow wanted Bert to run the business, he would not have the hassle. He had been off work almost a year. No private butchers were 'setting on'. The only 'Butcher work', was in supermarkets. He had been interviewed by three, all kids in their early twenties, checking on 'his' butchery knowledge. I can well image his expression and comments. In any case the meat arrived in the shop already cut, and jointed. It was just serving the piece the customer pointed to. He seemed to spend most of his time painting. I think the mermaid in the bathroom was fed up with the different positions he had painted her. His weight had shot up, he had let his hair grow, grown a 'baddy Mexican' type 'tash, and his bad eye was playing up. He now wore a black patch over it. He looked evil. Still the same old Bert, but as I told him many times. "Even I would not employ you looking like that." No effect at all.

But at the end of the day they would not take on any credit. Only dole coming in did not run to it.

Gerald from Smeeton called to ask if I would help teach his wife to drive. He had bought her a Hillman Husky to shop and go to work in. She had found the choke so handy to leave out, then she could hang her handbag on it. He insisted that she double de clutch, but she was not practical enough to get the hang of it. I told her to not bother, then more hassle from Sir.

It all soon came to a head one Sunday morning. I was coaching her driving whilst she was delivering battery hens' eggs for her Father. She was approaching a turn she must take, too fast, I waited, knowing she would change gear, but she hadn't. I shouted, she slammed the brakes on. Fifty six trays of two dozen eggs made the biggest omelette either of us had ever seen. That finished the lessons, in any case I had more than enough on with Dad etc.

Dad again, he had always been straight with money. It was said he would walk twenty miles to pay a penny debt, and twenty five to collect a half pence owing. Not any more, he would pay no one if he could possibly get away with it. Another chore to face, find and pay bills before the bailiffs arrived. Charlie's widow thought he was hoping for a comment in the paper as to how much he had left. Of course she no longer attempted to cook for him, she told me in the lane one day. But she admitted to being sorry for him and calling in to chat.

She surprised me with her parting shot. "May you live as long as you want to, and want to as long as you live."

Before I had left Dad, he had asked for a scarf? In midsummer? I could not find a single shop with one in stock. Marks was the final 'try'. The bright young thing behind the counter, lathered in make up, informed. "We an't got none duck."

"Well if you have not got none you must have some," I pointed out. Her blank look had me moving on. In desperation I gave Dad my best blue grey one. The following week I found the dog tied to a lamp post outside the post office. WITH MY SCARF!

Late on that year I caught a very bad cold, tried all the nice and not so nice cures without avail. The quack suggested the sensible and quickest cure was bed rest. Much against the grain but I realised the sense of it. I retired with a mug of rum, with a drop of milk and honey in it. I never knew if it did good, but it tasted well.

The next morning Gerald called. "Don't tell anyone youth, they will all want it."

The morning after, it was flu, no doubt at all, absolutely everything ached. The phone rang. Charlie's widow. She had found Dad passed out on the kitchen floor, she had sent for the ambulance and they had arrived within half an hour??? No, she did not know where they had taken him.

I gathered my aching bones, dressed, and set off sniffling. Nothing at the General. "If he is old, try the Community."

Blank looks, till I realised it was the old work house.

Out of visiting hours, but they let me in. A waste of time as he was out cold, and had been all the time. However, they were pleased to find 'someone' who could fill in their clipboard questions, two of. One for the house man, one for the male sister. The house doctor kept me over an hour. I gave him the full history. War action, shrapnel, pit accidents, back, foot, arms, legs, blood clots, temper, faddy, and 'different' style of eating.

What did I mean?

"Puddings, he will only eat, milk pudding and apple pie, he has both before his meat and veg."

"Why?"

"Dunno, my guess is it's a relic of the bad old days. They all had a garden, fruit trees, etc. So their Mother filled them with stodge, before so that they could not eat so much meat which had to be bought." The look on the chap's face had me realising it had all been a waste of time.

The big burly male sister stopped me on route for the

door. "Don't worry lad, we will look after him." He would have been more in place as a heavy weight boxer, size, looks. But like a lot of big men, no doubt as gentle as a kitten?

"Rather you than me," I just had to say. "He is difficult to handle."

"We are sure that he is under nourished, either not enough, or the wrong type of food. No matter, we will build up his vitamins with pills."

This brought a wry smile to my face. "You'll be busy. He either can't or won't take pills."

He put a hand on my shoulder. "I retire soon lad, I've done this job all my life, rest assured you Dad WILL have whatever he needs to make him well again. One way or another. Call and see him any time any day you want," was his kind comment as he opened the door for me.

I called at 'some time' every day, twice when at all possible, usually the first and last calls of the day. The greeting, (as usual) depending on 'his' mood.

The first time he showed real interest was when they had 'forced' him to take pills, and showed bumps on his head to prove the point. I checked with the nurses, yes, he had bumped his head on the wall, trying to dodge their pill laden hands. One complained he had knocked the pills far and wide, as he did not know 'where her hands had been before?'

Then the Father of one of my wife's school friends was admitted. Her Dad's bed was facing the door, my Dad's bed was facing the tap and bowl. When she was filling her Father's water carafe she would turn and ask.

"Hello Mr Chapman, is your Ron alright?"

"Never bloody see him do I?"

Back with her Dad, she would tell him. "Mr. Chapman says his Ron never calls to see him."

"Janet, he comes every day, twice when he can. He's always in a rush, but makes time to have a word with me every time."

The outcome, was of course inevitable. The phone call to say Dad had passed on arrived at bed time. "No need to come in tonight, tomorrow would do, bring a case for his clothes etc., and instructions as to whom would handle the funeral."

Before I could get to the sister's office, two young doctors accosted me. "Did you realise your Father had a very badly scarred foot, did I know why he had holes drilled in his head, he had a piece of metal buried in his shoulder, four vertebrae in his spine were very badly damaged."

Already considerably shattered. It took a great deal of control for me to evenly ask them. "Did they never ever read the bloody notes that had been meticulously written on his admittance to hospital?"

Fortunately (for them) the male sister arrived and saved 'their' day. Would I kindly step into his office? Seething, I complied.

With a wistful kindly smile, the sister began to speak.

"I retired yesterday, I've come in today especially to see you. I remember telling you that no patient has ever beaten me, they would get their medicine one way or another."

I could only nod, and wonder what was coming.

"Your Dad did, he was the strongest, most awkward stubborn cuss I have ever had to deal with."

I had to smile, this time at least, he had not let me down.

Chapter 31
Sweeping Up

It was weekend before I could find or make time to go down to Dad's place. A big surprise in store. There 'had been', around four tons of coal in the coal house, plus two more stacked at the side. All gone, not just gone, ALL the slack had been swept up as well. I looked into the outhouse, Mum's pride and joy, her little Prilect washing machine also GONE! I admit, both were outside and not locked up. But WHO?

Jane thought she knew straight away. "Charlie's widow," she announced, sure in her knowledge. But! other than an out and out accusation, insisting to look round her property. In any case, it was no doubt stached away some where else. In a way, it did not matter, we did not need either, we had gas central heating and our own washer, there had been that intended promise to the nice doctor. However, he was now in a modern house, with a new car, so did he no longer need or want? In time one always finds out who is true and the many who are not.

It was a small gathering at the Crematorium Chapel the next week. Two Aunts, one Uncle, a chap from t' pit, and two of my long standing friends was the sum total.

As I walked away from the chapel, it dawned on me just how Atlas must have felt when the weight of the world was taken from his shoulders. We all went home, had a chat, a drink, every one made the right noises and drifted off, all was peace. Whilst Jane made yet another pot of tea I gazed at the Jack Russell. Spread on the hearth rug, not a care in the world. Did she realise the

305

moods and temper were gone? All future was now regular food, and a clean bed from now on. Jane brought the tea in from the kitchen.

"You've remembered that I'm going out tonight?"

I hadn't.

It was an arrangement of long standing. One of her work friends had joined the pudding club and was having a leaving party.

"I shall be alright."

"There's no way I'm leaving you alone, tonight of all nights, equally there is no way I am going to let Sue down. I will phone her and see what we can arrange. Phoned, bathed, yet another shave, best suit, and we were on our way to a small country hotel with a good reputation at that time for steaks. I was introduced to almost thirty fresh faces, I suspect that I was the oldest present?. In such a crowd I was normally looked on as the 'chatter up', the one with the jokes, I tried a couple, both went flat. In any case it was not really the time for frivolity, I was the one that needed the jolt, they all acted as though they thought the brewery needed more profit.

I felt 'out of it', the usurper, so it seemed natural to drift towards the bar when the meal was finished.

The manageress was instructing a new recruit, what a recruit. Sixteen or seventeen. Tight jumper over a superb 'pair', her brown suede mini skirt was far too short. (who cares) the legs went on forever, perfect in every detail. Her hazel bobbed hair was ultra squeaky clean. A superb little dish.

"And what might you hope to be when you grow up? I asked.

She just blushed, and looked coy. The boss lady took over.

"She starts today on her Hotel Management Training course."

"What does that entail?"

She rattled off without hardly a single pause for breath.

"Serving drinks and meals at bar and table, keeping accounts, knowledge of cellar work, buying in supplies, controlling staff to keep the place clean, plus of course the most difficult of all." She paused, added an angelic smile before finishing. Making all customers including the smart Alecs feeling as though they really are wanted."

The barb did strike target. "So what will she do in her spare time?"

"That's when the last one really takes up time." Her 'lived in' face creased with laughter, her large bust trembled with effort to keep control of her amusement.

"That's what I could do with right now, I've had, to say the least a truly traumatic day. I have cremated my Father, not a happy time, but it has taken a load of worry off my shoulders. My wife is with the party in the dining room, the crowd are her work mates, I know no one, sore thumb springs to mind, so would it be possible for the young lady to attend to my needs at that corner table?"

"She's shy, you won't get much chat out of her."

"With a body like that who needs to talk?" I leered.

Management lost control and burst into laughter, the young lady blushed deeply.

"I think you could be the best introduction possible

for her on her first night, I don't doubt she will always remember it."

The girl was not looking very sure on how things were moving, even more so when the boss instructed. "Will you please attend to this gentleman's needs?" She then patted us both on the back and walked off, her shoulders shaking with laughter.

I gave the girl a wink, and wandered to the corner table, sat, and looked back. She was still standing beside the bar, very unsure. I curled my index finger at her. Almost with a jolt start, she scuttled over.

"You will need a pencil and pad." She almost trotted to the bar again. Her rear had a magnetic attraction, such a smooth rolling action She searched without finding, and shot through the door behind the bar, returning very soon with ball point and pad. "What sorts of whisky do you have?" She did run this time, through the door yet again. First back was the manageress, girl behind like a little lamb. They both turned their backs on me, arms waved and heads nodded as the boss no doubt pointed out the various optics and glasses. The boss waved a happy good bye to me and disappeared through 'her' door, the girl came back.

She almost chanted "Teacher's Bell's, White Horse." I shook my head at all. Her bottom lip almost trembled, her face was a picture, she really needed hugging and kissing.

"Black Bottle, Famous Grouse, Ballantynes, Grants, J. & B?"

Her face by now showed almost terror, she went through that door like a whirlwind.

308

The boss's head reappeared. "You've had your fun, what would you really like?"

"Grouse?"

"Coming up," and she was gone.

By now, I felt I had been a little unfair, so when she appeared with a new bottle of Grouse I called out. "With water if you please."

She did very well, there was a spare optic, she fitted the bottle, lifted a measure into a whisky glass, BUT! filled it with water. By now I felt like a real heel. With a kindly smile I explained that if she searched, she would find a jug, into which she could put water, then I could put my own water into my whisky.

So started an evening I shall long cherish. Grouse, a very pretty girl attending, who listened to my 'chat' with interest, laughed at the right times, and without realising, was learning how to cope with dirty minded older men. Plus! she was getting me over Dad.

Her Father was a policeman, her Mother worked in a Nottingham office, her one elder brother had just joined the R.A.F. They had fought like cat and dog whilst he was at home, but she was now missing him greatly. She loved cooking, and hoped to learn to cook 'special' meals. She had a good friend who was a boy, they liked dancing, listening to records, and country walks. They had never ever kissed, and she did not want to????

The evening passed all too quickly for me, but of course wife and gang had came to collect me. I rose to my feet, and had to hang on to my chair. My new friend helped support me.

"One more question if I may before you go sir?" I

grinned down at her with raised eyebrows.

"What advice would you give to make a relationship a long and happy one?"

"Always tell each other the truth, and never ever put perfume on any part that you hope will get kissed."

We kissed a long goodbye kiss to the wolf whistles of the envious men in the crowd. Giggling through colour she confided. "You know, you are really nice now that I know you."

"I know, what a pity that only you and I realise the fact."

The manageress took my arm to the door. "Many thanks for your help, I don't know what you have told her, but she's grown up already. I do hope that your wife will drive you home?"

"Of corsh." A grinning Jane took my other arm with an amused smile at the manageress and took me out.

Chapter 32
Everybody Treats Me Rotten

Jane went to work in the morning and left me in bed. I felt like a robber's dog. Sort of 'surfaced' about lunch time, had pills and tea for breakfast. Two cigarettes later I felt fit enough to go to Mrs. Wells.

She asked. Did I like Hazlenuts?

"Yes, they are my favourite nut."

She presented me with a sweet bag full.

Stock sorted, a list of 'wants' made out, I set off to the COOP for cigarettes, much cheaper than the corner shop. I met Eric coming back from the same errand. Chewing steadily I asked if he fancied a nut.

"Mrs. Wells?"

"Yes,"

"No thanks." He went on his way grinning his fool head off.

Dot England arrived, "What's amusing him?" Nodding after Eric.

"Dunno, want a nut?"

"Mrs. Wells?"

"Yes."

"No thanks." She tucked her arm through mine and walked me on. "Listen, Mrs Wells likes chocolate, but with her teeth nuts and hard chocolate are not possible. So she buys chocolate hazelnuts, sucks the chocolate off, and re bags the nuts." Giggling she went on. "You must write that book, but don't put my proper name in it."

To say the least I felt more queasy than ever. I took the dog up the forest, distributed the nuts to birds, squirrels, the lot. They did not seem to mind, but I did not tell them what I had been told.

Next job, go and check Dad's bungalow. No sign of a sale, plenty interested, but no mortgage available. One wanted it for land only at half my asking price as they were going to knock it down to rebuild. Wait and hope a bit longer.

It looked neglected, un wanted, desolate, and scruffy. Almost in tears I thought back to the effort it had cost us all. Raising the money, painting, decorating, altering, Dad struggling in the garden, Mum fighting up the three back steps on her two sticks. I left it, and walked back up the lane. Charlie's widow came out of her garden gate. Since the doubt about the coal and washer, I 'had to' rather than 'wanted to', be polite.

"Your Dad wanted me to marry him. He was going to take me to France to find two gallon jars of rum he had hidden during the war."

"One down a well, t'uther in a rotten old apple tree?" She seemed surprised, I enjoyed this. "If the apple tree was rotten in fourteen eighteen it will now be long gone. How would he get down the well? He can't swim anyway. IF it's not been filled in. He was scared still of boats, and terrified of flying. He's been waiting for the Channel Tunnel as long a I can remember. We are still waiting for it."

Not to be out done she went on. "If I had have married him, the few quid he left would have been mine now, AND the bungalow."

I almost said. "Well you will have to settle for the coal and the washer then." But held my council.

"You know he wanted to be buried, he was scared stiff of being cremated?"

For a few seconds that horrified me, then realised it was Dad's own fault. He should have told me, not a neighbour, then she should have told me. Then I almost smiled. This was the one and only time that he had ever not had his own way.

We parted with her last pithy comment.

"Nob'dy will ever buy it looking like that, apart from which, that garden looks as though it has never ever seen a spade."

Walking away, I realised how right she was, thought, I must make the effort and make time to do it. No time or sense in trying to grow anything. 'I will dig all the weeds in', I promised myself.

Early morning (for me) I had started digging before nine a.m. Sunday. That clay land was hard and heavy, it was well over a year now since a spade had touched it. Last summer had been a warm one, baked clay. Not good for a wimp of a credit draper, with too much belly, and too many fags. Short of time as usual, I was going at it hammer and tongues, when, 'THAT' pain struck again! I struggled home, bathed, and put myself to bed. Jane was out, but I could not think for the life of me where she had said she was going. Nor could I think what to do for the best. Think? I must have been almost in a coma? Possibly I slept? No pain just lying, only worry.

She arrived, "What's up?"

I started to explain, she set off at a rush for the phone, I don't remember how I stopped her, but I did, so she phoned Eric.

Round he came, full of concern, but as jovial as ever.
"Scared of doctor and driving licence?" A limp nod.
"No treatment last time? Head shake.
"You just need rest."
"Don't be so b." His huge hand covered my mouth, stopping any further protestations.

"Shurrup and listen." I opened my mouth, his hand lifted again, threatening. Jane and I can pull in your 'less reliables', the good ones will pay double next week. I've now got a caravan on the East Coast, temporary, but it's empty, you can look after it for a week. Must explain. I fitted a chap with an aid months ago. He wanted, needed, the best, but could not afford. His grand daughter was getting married, he needed money for her present, and wanted to hear the ceremony, so I let him have the aid on deposit only and said he could pay me whenever. He did not agree, not business like. We haggled for ages, the outcome was. He has a caravan on the East Coast, not used it since his wife died, eldest daughter goes over once a month to clean and make sure all is well. It's mine until he pays what he owes, he can't pay now, he's dead. It's mine till I sell it and give the family the balance. You have almost three weeks before the bills are due, so your going to go and have a week's rest in it. I will drive you over, so that all you can do is eat, sleep, and walk."

Jane interrupted. "But what if it is a heart attack?"

"It's not, or they would have treated him last time, AND stopped him from driving. He's pulled a chest muscle again. A wimp like him should not be trying to do hard work." His smile took any possible 'sting' out of the words. His face suddenly lit up. "It's a bank holiday anyway, his takings will be well down, no matter what he does."

Jane's deep voice, full of relief, said. "As usual, he's right, you know."

"Get yoursen a case packed, I will pick you up in an hour." He went.

Jane and I looked at each for minutes before laughing, as we realised, he would never ever change.

I had another bath, shaved, and almost felt human. Shaving in the mirror with time to think, I looked at myself. He could well be right. Face gaunt, hair all but gone, I was ageing, FAST! Eric is right, I need a break.

Eric was still a very polished driver, smooth, fast, all his judgment's spot on. It was relaxing to just sit, and let us go past the world. I began to think, had I brought all my 'wanteds'.

Sleeping bag, lining, spare clothes, shaving tackle, towels, some tinned food (just in case)

Eric's words broke into my thoughts. "If you can't cook for yourself, you will have to eat out. I know a couple of Dolly birds who would love to have come and looked after you, but on second thoughts I realised it is nourishment that you need, not punishment."

I looked across at him with a smile, but his face was deadly serious, he meant it.

Getting near now, Trixie in the back knew before us, she had smelled the sea. She moved from window to window, searching for it, her tail just a blur. Very little traffic 'our way', most seemed to be on their way back. The dog still looking, was subdued by a growled "Down girl," from me, even though the tail still wagged at a hundred miles an hour. Eric swung the car into the park of an interesting looking 'eatery', they served us with a superb high tea. Eric seemed to know all the waitresses, and they certainly all knew him???

Then on to the caravan, which in spite of its 'lack of use', looked very pristine to me. He carried in the bedding, whilst I brought my 'bits and bobs'. Between us we found the mains water tap, the electric main switch, turned on the huge, almost full, gas bottle. Tested the oven and four burners on the cooker, lit the gas fridge, then after a struggle we got the gas water heater 'fired up'. Finally, he produced a new bottle of 'Grouse' and made me promise there would be 'some' left when he returned to pick me up next week end. Then with a friendly 'pretend' cuff around the ear, he left.

I took the dog on the lead into the next field for her evening toilet, no way would I risk her off the lead with the sea so near. She was well and truly all agog. At the last minute I remembered to give her a basin of water, before turning in. It was still light.

Almost twelve hours later my eyes opened, I almost felt human. The appealing dancing dog reminded me. I had not brought any dog meat. We both had to manage with toast, yes I had brought margarine, but no marmalade, or cereals!

Minutes only to wash the few pots, the dog was now desperate for her morning 'toilet'. On the lead into the next field for starters, we then set off for the beach. She knew, really knew. Pulling, prancing, on back legs only at times, she almost dragged me along. We approached the promenade. Now it really was 'long arm' time. As we approached the concrete 'walk down' to the beach, a family with a Boxer dog came up. The owner took a stick off the dog, leaned it on the tubular fence before walking away. I waved and called "thanks", and picked it up.

That really 'turned her on' if she was hyper active before she was now almost beserk. It was difficult to keep her still enough to remove her lead. Almost like having a maggot on the end. Free at last, she danced on her back legs backwards, watching the stick. Back went my arm for the throw, but I had to delay, a family walked across my throwing field. A seagull flew over my shoulder, over the dog, she turned and chased it. So fast it was almost a blur. Had she thought the gull was the stick? The seagull swooped low, the dog in hot pursuit, followed by a little mite swaddled in a mass of woollies who toddled behind gurgling "Goggy." It was all so ludicrous, I had to wipe my eyes. The gull swept over a breakwater, the dog hurdled after it, the toddler fell over it. It was almost like a cartoon. All very amusing until a female voice screamed.

"MY BABY"

I ran as hard as I could, when I got nearer I was appalled to realised it was NOT a breakwater, but the side of a culvert about ten feet wide. I looked over, there was the baby in quite a brisk stream, floating on its back, still chuckling, and gurgling "Goggy." It was rapidly being washed out to sea!!! The dog was trying to scramble up the timber culvert side. Down to the water was a five foot drop, no idea of its depth, it was to say the least, 'Unclean'. so I dare not dive, a jump was also risky. I turned and ran towards the sea, tearing off clothes as I went. Down to vest, underpants, shoes and socks, I got to the sea, kicked off the shoes and went in at full chat with my version of a running shallow dive. For the few strokes I could do a hissing crawl round the end of what I had thought was the breakwater, then changed to a solid sidestroke against the stream. My crawl 'looked' good, but I could only manage twenty yards at that pace (still without breathing) The dog seemed pleased to see me, I went past it, it turned to follow me, seemingly well in charge of the situation. I spluttered at her "Back Girl," Wonder of wonders she turned on the one and only instruction. I swooped the child up in my arms, and with some trepidation let my feet drop, they touched bottom at shoulder depth.

A scream from above made me look up. The frantic Mother was peering down at us. "It's alright, I've got him, he's alright, I'll bring him round the end."

"It's a she," the Mother wailed, trotting alongside, as I waded seawards with as long a stride as I could. Within yards however the water was getting too deep for wading, and I was meeting waves. I hooked the baby in the crook of my left arm and went on the side stroke again, looked into that little cherubic face. It answered with the sweetest smile ever, and murmured "Goggy".

The next sense to hit me was the smell, it was evil, I glanced around, the reason was obvious, I was swimming in raw sewage, all evidence was apparent. We swam around the end together, the dog must have waited?? Mother was ploughing towards me, well over knee deep in water. "Go back," I spluttered, "No need to get wet." She came on regardless. The Culvert sides were lined with clapping people as we waded ashore. Mother almost snatched the baby from me. Tears of relief streaming down her face, then seemed at a loss, should she rush off with her baby or thank me. I took her arm and steered her on to dry land, whilst 'clucking' encouragement to the Russell paddling steadily behind. As soon as the dog was on sand, she shook, gave all around an unwanted shower. Thinking, I realised that the air trapped in the baby's cellular clothes had probably kept her afloat, but what had kept her the right way up?

Mother and baby were heading for the prom at a good lick, I found a shoe and slipped it on to a soggy sock, no sign of the other. Then a Border Terrier rushed by with it, pursued by a tall rangy good looking young man. He caught it, rescued my shoe, handed it over with a rueful grin. "Sorry mate, he's got a thing about shoes, your a very good swimmer."

With a rueful look over the culvert side, the only reply I could think of was. "Well, let's say I went through the motions." I collected clothes piece by piece and followed Mother and baby up to the promenade. She was sat on the lea side of a shelter, out of the now keen east wind, I noticed and realised we were all shivering.

She had taken the outer soggy garments off the child, and I was surprised to note that the under garments were almost dry, but her little feet pods were drenched. Mother removed them and began to dry the little feet with a clean nappy. Glancing at me she handed over another of the same. "Sorry, it's all I have," with a wan half smile. "I never dreamed we would get wet today."

We exchanged a sort of small shy smile as she

dabbed at the youngster whilst I did what I could with that puny bit of cloth.

Busy rubbing at my thighs, I watched the Mother dabbing at the little toes from above and below. The child's toes were webbed! "I've never seen that on anyone else," I started.

"She gets them from me." Slipping off a sodden sandal to prove the point.

"Snap," I replied, bearing one of mine.

"Do you live here? I really need to thank you properly."

"No, I come from a small mining village in East Midshire. It's almost in Sherwood Forest. I've had a health scare and a friend has brought me for a week's rest in his caravan."

"Not near Dubdy Common?" Her tone and voice indicated it could not possibly be. I could only nod.

"The very same," I assured her.

"My Mam and Dad used to live there, he worked at the pit, but they moved to Boston before I was born." Then she sniffed in distaste. "I do hope you're not going to inherit your Grandad's sweaty feet, Petal." She almost scolded the child as she sniffed again in disgust. She turned to me. "Dad had the most dreadful sweaty feet, glad to say mine don't."

With a half smile I explained that the water in the culvert had not been exactly fresh.

"You don't mean that it's..."

I laughed and nodded.

She pulled a face and said "Uggggh."

"Where are your Mum and Dad now?" I asked.

Looking intently at the brown eyes, the squeaky clean brown hair, the shape of her features.

"We lost Dad just over two years ago, pit dust on his lungs, and he smoked. He was in very poor health when he gave me away at my wedding. One month celebrating a wedding, two months later attending a funeral, why does it happen like that? Me Mam lasted two months after this little cherub was born." Nodding with obvious pride down at the still gurgling youngster. Her face clouded. "She took ill a week before she died, the doctors did not seem to know what was wrong. I asked her what she thought was wrong. she gave a funny reply, said she thought it might be a broken heart. That took some believing as they were always falling out." Just a suspicion of a tear formed.

I could only think to say "Sorry."

"You know what they say?" I shook my head. "When a new baby arrives, an old one has to go to make room." I had not heard that before. She visibly brightened, she had finished changing what she could for the baby and began to rub her own legs briskly.

I 'mopped' myself as best I could with my by now 'soggy nappy'.

"My husband is a driving instructor in Boston, he brought us here in an hour gap between lessons, things are quiet just now, he has another 'spare' hour about now to fetch us home.

The sky appeared to darken, we both looked up, a big man, a really big man loomed over us. Very tall and broad, a pencil moustache, steely grey eyes. She scrambled to her feet, started to gabble explanations, introduce me, got it all mixed up. I took over and gave him a rough guide as to what had happened.

It seemed to take ages for it all to be taken in as to what really had happened. When light dawned he scooped the child from her, berated her for not taking more care, whilst cuddling and cooing at the now bewildered baby. She burst into tears. That did it. "Come on now, quick, she must be given a warm bath, dry clothes, seen by a doctor." Holding the child close he just turned and went.

She turned to face me. "Sorry about that, he's so brusque at times, but he really does love our baby. I can never ever thank you enough for what you did, I'm so grateful." Lifting on to her tip toes she kissed me full on the lips. It was electric. Her mouth smelled and tasted so clean and fresh, so familiar. She took my hand in hers, dry, cool, small, it was all very disturbing and familiar. Then she turned and trotted after her husband's retreating broad back.

I stood, transfixed for ages, till the cold began to bite, I really was shivering now. I finished dressing as best I could, clipped the lead on a dithering dog, and very very deep in thought began to head back to the caravan. Uncomfortable? YES! My wet underpants had already seeped through my trousers. I thought if anyone 'sees', they will think I have wet myself. My soggy socks 'squelched' in my shoes. At long last we got to the caravan site. Hundreds of vans, in rows, all painted green and cream. I had remembered row five caravan G, but could not find it.

A wizened little man, skin like tanned leather, skinny

little legs poking out of shorts too short and legs too wide. A bald head with long hair on each side, he was constantly trying to sweep the long hair over the bald part. I enquired, he laughed. "Tha wants row G caravan five. It's rate be'ind yer."

I found a plug for the shower tray in a kitchen drawer. The full shower tray gave me almost six inches of water in which to bath Trixie, she was not at all keen, but I managed to get her clean, as dry as possible, and 'pegged' her lead loop outside with a tent peg, also from a kitchen drawer. Had a good shower myself, then reached out of the compartment for my towel that I had hung on a hook. In came a shivering dog. Lead and peg still connected. "Soft sand," I assumed, but I was feeling light headed. I sat in the shower tray and cuddled her, began to realise how tired I felt. Suppose it really has been one of those days, I remember thinking as my eyes closed. The dog's eyes had been closed for some minutes.

At that time I was not aware. The hot water heater had not been serviced, a Wren had built her nest in the air intake last spring, Carbon Monoxide has no smell or taste.

Thunderous knocking on the caravan side. The site warden had wondered why a caravan that was not supposed to be occupied had a wide open door. He had dragged us both out into the fresh air. My first realisation was of a cloth over my mouth and some strange man trying to kiss me. "Not bloody likely," I tried to say and lashed out, then Trixie was all over me, licking my face. I pushed her away, sense was returning, a man with a bleeding nose was holding my arms, and I was not wearing a stitch of clothing, a crowd was gathered round, just looking. Any pride I may have ever had, just went!